P9-DGE-111

Christmas '81

To Grandma Lilley

Love Ian

& Wendy

TEN CENTS OFF PER DOZEN

a Gregory Clark Omnibus

TEN CENTS OFF PER DOZEN
a Gregory Clark Omnibus

OPTIMUM PUBLISHING COMPANY LIMITED
Montreal · Toronto

The stories published in this book were originally published in Weekend Magazine.
Some excerpts included in the introduction were first published in a *Weekend Magazine* article entitled *In the Still of the Typewriter* by Blaik Kirby
Compiled by: Anna Ozvoldik
Design: Suzanne Vincent Poirier
Illustrations: Jack Tremblay
Photographs: Montreal Star/Canada Wide

Copyright©Optimum Publishing Company Limited 1979

Published by Optimum Publishing Company Limited, Montreal

All rights reserved. No part of this book may be reproduced in any manner whatsoever without the prior written permission of the publisher.

Legal deposit-4th trimester 1979
Bibliothèque Nationale du Québec

For information, contact:
Optimum Publishing Company
245 rue St.-Jacques,
Montreal, Quebec
H2Y 1M6
Michael S. Baxendale, Director

ISBN 0-88890-116X

Printed and bound in Canada

Contents

Introduction

Greg Clark has captivated readers for years. The man was as charming as his stories. But we, who must introduce him, are not storytellers, and cannot spin a yarn about the man as he could about us. And so we let Greg Clark introduce himself.

*"Personally, I never read prefaces.
Being human, I naturally suppose
that nobody else does. Therefore I
shall keep it short."*

*"I am essentially a very modest, retiring and unambitious man. I never
entertained any particular ambition. What I have is all I want. I find that my
rich friends are the most troubled, and my poor friends the happiest. That's
been true all through my life."*

"I used to infuriate the great Fred Griffin, a meticulous reporter, by coming in and sitting down and starting a story right away. I never had to throw a page away. But I wasn't a newspaperman, I was a storyteller. That story I was writing, I'd told it to myself over and over until it was word-perfect."

"When the First World War came, I tried to enlist and was repeatedly turned down because I was too small. At the same time, the paper kept losing the reporters who were covering recruiting; all of them enlisted. I asked for the job. I spent about six months working under Colonel Le Grand Reed of the 9th Mississauga Horse. I quoted him every day and got pictures of him in the paper at least once a week. I wrote speeches for him. I had the gift of the gab, really. One day he looked at me and said: 'Greg I think you're up to something.' And I said 'How did you guess?' And he said 'When do you want to go?' And I said 'April Fool's Day'."

"My battalion reached the crest at 7:05 A.M. I was the only surviving officer, and my company and I had the proud distinction of leading its first platoon across the crest to establish a Lewis-gun strong point down that steep, brushy, wooded hill.
The sleet and snow miraculously ceased, the sun came out. It was a stupendous sight. There below us, like the kingdoms of the earth, lay the Douai plain for miles.
And I thought it was symbolic —ah, that's the word!—symbolic, that we had done it at Easter.
As far as I could see, south, north, along the miles of Ridge, there were the Canadians. And I experienced my first full sense of nationhood."

"...early in the Depression the editor looked over the "Star Weekly" and found it was full of serious news. The only cheerful thing was a cartoon by Jimmy Frise. The orders came down to get a second Frise piece in to brighten the paper. The editor said 'Who's going to do it?' and they all pointed at me, and there I was, stuck with the greatest piece of good fortune that ever befell me. I decided then that someone should sit in the corner and play marbles, just to help the reader keep his balance."

13

"I knew I had got him. You see, Ralph thought he had caught the biggest fish and he had left this fish in a pond he had built at the edge of the lake, and that night why, that night some unknown renegade went in the dark and let that fish loose. So the next day when we judged the fish Ralph was terribly upset when my fish was the biggest."

"Fishing is the least objectionable way of doing nothing."

"*I've heard it said that I manipulated things, made 'em happen. I didn't. I think things just do happen.*

And my purpose in writing about them is that of a troubadour, or one of those travelling storytellers who, in olden time, went from village to village, to regale; to celebrate the sheer joy of life in terms of life's simplest things, the daily bread of life.

'I just read such and such a story,' people exclaim to me. 'That is exactly what happened to me last month!'
Sure. Only they didn't understand it was a story. If we only realized it, every day of our lives is a story."

Ten Cents Off Per Dozen

I DON'T KNOW about you fellows," said Herriot at the lunch table, "but I'm going to take it pretty easy in the New Year."

"Diet?" I supposed, because he had eaten only mushrooms on toast, and no cream or sugar in his coffee.

"No," said Herriot, "I mean financially."

"Now, look here," put in Cooper, "if you start talking poor like that, the first thing you know you're going to START a recession! If everybody pulls in their horns..."

"I'm just referring to my immediate circumstances," explained Herriot. "We went nuts in my family this Christmas. All of a sudden, we just went nuts, and threw our money around like confetti."

"Aw, well," said Skipper Howard, "we've all got to ease up for a few weeks after Christmas."

"That's why we have January sales," I pointed out. "Everybody eases up for a little while, and then BOING! Out come the January sales, and away we go again."

"My secretary," said Herriot, "has an uncle who runs one of these chicken farms. It's about 30 miles out of town. He produces thousands of eggs per diem."

"Ugh!" said Skipper.

For if there is anything you shouldn't mention, or even think about, in the week between Christmas and New Year's Day, it is a soft-boiled egg.

"She tells me," pursued Herriot, "that you can get new-laid eggs, laid this very day, at 10 cents off per dozen if you call there."

"Please," said Cooper. "We've all got a great big New Year's dinner to eat this weekend!"

"It's a lovely day," said Herriot.

Herriot has a station wagon equipped with snow tires, Scottish tartan lap robes and a remarkable heating system.

"How about it?" he asked.

"Listen," said Cooper, "if you buy six dozen eggs, you save 60 cents. How much will it cost you to drive out to this chicken farm?''

"It would impress our wives," commented Skipper, "if we came home with a great big basket of fresh eggs at 10 cents off per dozen.''

Well, you know how it is during the holiday week. Nobody is really working.

"Be at my office at 3," said Herriot.

It was a lovely day, sunny and keen and blue and white. Sitting in Herriot's beautiful station wagon, with the windows slightly open, the heater on and the tartan lap robes tucked around our legs, it was the next best thing, the nearest thing, to riding in a one-horse open sleigh.

When we left the highway 15 miles out of town and turned on to a secondary road, the sound of the snow tires on the new-fallen snow was music. At no time except in early May, when the country landscape is just flowing into its purest green, do the fields look so magical as in early winter: the shapes of the fences, the aloof houses standing lonely but snug, the sweep of the hills, the dark mystery of the woodlots in the distance, the absence of all life—no cattle, no dogs, no men. The sky seems so high.

"This is glorious," said Skipper.

"Herriot, old boy," I said, "even if we didn't get 10 cents off, it would be worth it."

And we didn't get 10 cents off.

After inquiring at a crossroads gas station, we found our way to the chicken farm. Behind a standard farmhouse spread an encampment of squat buildings silent in the winter sunset, for it was nearing 5 P.M.

At the farmhouse, a man told us he sold no eggs.

"My eggs," he said, kindly, "are all contracted for.''

"But your niece, Mary," said Herriot, "my secretary, told me to come out any time..."

"Oh," exclaimed the farmer, "you must be Mr. Hairtonic or Hairdo, is it?"

"Herriot," said Herriot. "And she told me we could get eggs for 10 cents a dozen off the retail price.''

"I could let you have a few," said the farmer, "at five cents off.''

"Well, my friends here," said Herriot, "could use a few too.''

"Mmmm," said the farmer. "I wouldn't want it to get around. I sell my entire output to the one jobber. His truck has just left with the day's production.''

A woman appeared beside the farmer's shoulder.

"For Mary's friend," she said, "you ought to be able to scrape up a few."

He scraped up 16 dozen.

Four dozen each.

Saving: 20 cents apiece.

I suggested we go with him to have a look at a modern chicken farm. But he regretted that it was against his policy to exhibit his premises to visitors in winter, due to the disturbance of temperature and the agitation of the hens at this time of night.

For it was dark by the time he came back with the eggs.

"Sorry I haven't any egg cartons," he said. "I'll just put 'em in six quart baskets, eh? Four dozen each."

We placed the baskets in the back of the station wagon.

Strange how completely the beauty of the world vanishes when you are looking down a tunnel of headlights.

"I told my wife," I mentioned, "that I would be home between 6:30 and 7."

"We'll make it," said Herriot, swerving out of the lane and on to the secondary road.

In 20 minutes we were back on the highway.

"Well," said Skipper, "it was a nice way to end the Old Year, even if we only saved 20 cents each."

"Money isn't everything," agreed Herriot, stepping on the gas and letting the big station wagon feel its oats on the black bare pavement of the highway.

In another 20 minutes, we could see the glow of the city ahead.

In another 10, we were coming to the first stoplight intersections of the outlying suburbs.

A panel truck was ahead of us as we neared the intersection.

The yellow light came on.

The truck accelerated as though to dash across.

Herriot accelerated on its tail.

Suddenly the truck jammed on its brakes.

We crashed into it. Sixteen dozen eggs catapulted from the flat platform of the back of the station wagon, up, over, in lovely swift arcs on to the low rich-upholstered seats of the wagon.

Slightly dazed, I unwound my tartan robe, opened the door and stepped out, wiping egg from the back of my head, my neck, my ears, my shoulders.

From two and then three cars that came behind, people bailed out and came running.

"Oh, heavens!" cried the first to come near me.

And he backed away, shielding his eyes with his arm.

Skipper got out the rear door, head bowed, wiping. From the far side, I could hear a hubbub.

"Doctors! Get doctors! Internal injuries! Poor devils! All crushed, their insides all over!"

"Eggs!" I heard Herriot's voice rising. "EGGS!"

"Never mind your legs," a strong kind voice came over the car top. "Poor fellow, you're burst wide open!"

In the glare of the headlights from behind, other rescuers rushed up, recoiled, then came horrified closer to me, and timid hands seized my sleeves to try to get me to lie down, poor, poor exploded fellow, my viscera coiling off me . . .

Well, we got home about 7:45. It took that long to untangle the station wagon and the truck, neither much damaged; and to scrape each other off and wipe the seats with the tartan rugs and so forth.

"It's a nice way," called Skipper, stickily, as we drew up at my house and I got out of the station wagon, "to end the Old Year!"

Thanks

NOT MANY of the shop windows were lighted, not even in the big stores. It was gently snowing, the kind that drops straight down. A lovely night to walk, after dinner, along the downtown streets while making up your mind whether to go to a movie.

Snow that falls soft as feathers like this creates a festive, an old-fashioned feeling, far different from the effect of blizzard snow that makes you tuck your chin in. I looked kindly at the other pedestrians in the street lights, and they looked kindly at me. For two pins we would all have cried a happy New Year to one another if New Year's hadn't been gone. It was that kind of a night.

Two blocks from where I got off the downtown bus I saw a crowd gathered in front of one of the few brightly-lighted shop windows. They were laughing and gesticulating, and as I approached, I could hear girls squealing.

Due to my small size, I have long since given up trying to see what crowds are interested in. Unless I can get ringside seats given to me by the management or promoters, I never go where crowds go. For instance, I haven't had a look in one of those Christmas windows full of little animated manikins since I got too heavy to be lifted up on somebody's shoulders.

With my usual benevolent air of indifference, I was in the act of passing around the crowd pushing and exclaiming before the big window when I heard a girl's voice:

"It's ALIVE!" she screamed. "EEEeeeee!"

I halted.

"There's TWO of them!" came another voice loud amidst the laughter and chatter of the crowd.

I think even so I would have pushed on my way if two or three other passers-by had not barged in and shoved me into the crush.

"What is it?" I asked another short person I found in the thick of it.

"Mice," he said.

So I let those on the outside keep pushing until in due time I was bunted through to the window.

It was a ladies'-wear window ablaze with pink and silver light, and charming with a beautiful display of lingerie—orchid, shell pink, virginal white. It had the usual dainty announcements on cards about the post-Christmas bargains. Scattered in careless elegance amid the diaphanous garments were sparkling necklaces, earrings, jewelled purses, radiant compacts. And disporting themselves amongst all this loveliness were two fat mice.

Festive mice. Darting, twiddling, jumping, dirty, dark gray little mice with glossy large bug eyes.

"EEEeeeek!" cried the women around me. "EEEE-eeeee!"

That is the traditional sound women make on seeing mice.

One mouse ran up the sleeve of a shadow-blue bed jacket.

"Geeeek!" cried a woman. "Let me OUT of here!"

No ballet dancers with the stage all to themselves ever performed a more spectacular *pas de deux*. They darted. They stopped. They vanished. They reappeared. They explored a pair of silken slippers, inside the toe.

"Gaaaahhhh!" gagged a female voice back of me.

Around, up, back of, under, the gracefully-draped lingerie the mice darted with fascinating figures a skater might envy.

"This," said a man squeezed beside me, "could ruin the business of this shop."

He was a fine ruddy citizen. We exchanged citizenly glances of respect.

"If enough women come by here," he said, "it can be all over town by the day after tomorrow."

"I suppose," I supposed.

"What we ought to do," he said, "is contact the owners. If this keeps up for another hour, with all this lighting, and all this mob gathered around, there is no telling what injury can be done this store."

"Maybe," I suggested, "we could get hold of the night watchman."

"Ah," said the citizen. I could see that he recognized in me the executive, the man of action.

Being an old soldier, I know how to attack.

The citizen and I bucked our way out of the idle throng.

"There'll be a lane," I asserted, "around at the back."

22

We hustled up through the sweet snow to the corner and turned left, in expectation of a lane.

There was no lane.

"We could hammer on the front door," suggested the citizen.

"No night watchman," I assured, "pays attention to hammering on doors."

"Maybe," said the citizen, "we could find the name of somebody connected with the firm from the phone book."

"What's the name of the firm?" I checked.

So we hustled back through the straight-falling snow, and by standing on tip toes at the back of the mob, now larger than ever, we made out the shop's name: Thumblediffer's.

In a cigar store across the street we found a pay phone.

We looked up Thumblediffer's.

There it was, street number and all.

And right below it Thumblediffer, J. W.

We dialled a swift call to Mr. J. W. Thumblediffer.

A woman answered.

"Mr. Thumblediffer in?" I asked crisply.

"No," said the lady, languidly, "he's at a meeting."

"Can you tell us where?" I asked. "It's urgent."

"He's speaking at the meeting," said the woman. "Guest speaker."

"Where is it?" I demanded. "Madam, it is urgent. There are mice in his shop window..."

"EEEeeek!" said the woman.

"The shop window, all lighted up," I cried, "and mice scampering around in front of a great big gathering of passers-by..."

She gave us the name of the hotel.

We dialled the hotel and got the bell captain.

We explained to him that a Mr. Thumblediffer was addressing a meeting. "It will be the ladies'-wear convention," said the bell captain.

"Right!" I cried. "Get him to the phone as fast as you can."

He was gone four minutes.

"Mr. Thumblediffer," said the bell captain, "is in the midst of his address, and told me to take your number."

"Tell him," I shouted, "there are mice in his show window and a crowd of a hundred people..."

"Hang up," said the citizen.

I hung up.

The cigar store also sold hot coffee.

The citizen and I had a paper cup of hot coffee and watched out the window at the ever-shifting crowds in front of Thumblediffer's Ladies' Wear.

Suddenly, the store's lights went out.

The citizen and I hurried across. As the crowd thinned and drifted away, a man let himself out of the shop door.

"Thumblediffer?" I asked. "We're the ones who called you at the hotel."

"You!" said Mr. Thumblediffer, swelling up.

"There were crowds of people, dozens and dozens..." I began.

"Do you know what happened?" cried Mr. Thumblediffer. "When I saw that bellhop pushing his way between the tables the second time, I held up my hand and called to him from the platform. And at the top of his lungs he yelled that I had better come, there were mice in my display window."

"Well, you got here," I remarked.

"In front of the whole industry," wailed Mr. Thumblediffer, "he yells I got mice in my display window."

He turned his back and walked off into the snow without even saying thanks.

I shook hands with my fellow citizen.

And I didn't bother to go to a movie.

Elevator Man

MASTERS looked so gloomy when I encountered him on the street at lunch time a week ago last Friday that I suggested we have lunch together.

Now you understand we ordinary newspapermen, reporters, desk men and so forth, do not presume to offer advice. That is for the editorial writers. We "working" newspapermen, as we are called, to distinguish us from the intellectuals of our profession, merely offer sympathy. And we are pretty good at it, too, after having devoted the major part of our lives to woe.

Masters was full of woe. But we had hardly sat down at the restaurant table before I realized I was out of my depth.

His trouble was business.

"Haven't you heard?" he asked hollowly. "I'm going to be let out. They're going to fire me."

"Aw, no!"

For 15 years Masters has been manager of a tidy little bond and security business in which he grew up. He has about 20 people under him, office men, customer's men, counter girls, stenogs.

"You see, Greg," he said, "this tremendous boom in Canada isn't as good for some of us as you might think. It has put a lot of pressure on."

"Well, all you have to do is ask for more help, eh?"

"They've given me," sighed Masters, "all the help I could use. More. I've put two girls on the switchboard. But it is always in a panic. The whole place is full of impatient, disgruntled, irritated customers. We don't seem to be able to handle the job."

"So?"

"I've had my ultimatum," said Masters grimly. "If I can't get things running smoothly and get our customers in a better frame of mind, I'm out in six months. January first."

"Have you consulted the elevator man yet?" I inquired.

"The what?" demanded Masters.

"How many elevators have you in your building?"

"Just the one."

"Run by a man?"

"Yes," said Masters, puzzled.

"What kind of a guy is he?"

"Fiftyish, sixtyish," said Masters. "A shut-mouth, speechless sort of old boy. Been there as long as I can remember."

"Good, good!" I enthused. "Now, you know, Masters, the elevator man knows more about the business in his building than anybody else. He hears five hundred, a thousand conversations every day. He knows more about your staff than you ever will. He knows your customers inside out, hearing them going up and coming down."

"So what?" protested Masters.

"When I was a reporter," I explained, "I always started with the elevator man. You stay after hours tonight, and ask the old boy up to your office. Give him a cigar. Confess your problem to him. Tell him the whole story."

"Are you nuts?" asked Masters.

"I'm telling you!" I assured him hotly. "The trouble with you businessmen is that you are too lofty. As the famous saying is, you would rather lose ten thousand dollars than any of the stuffing out of your shirts."

"That isn't fair from you, Greg," said Masters, hurt, and thinking of all our fishing trips.

However, at 9 o'clock that night, Masters phoned me at the house, very excited.

"Well!" he shouted. "I had your elevator man up!"

"And?"

"I'll tell you later."

Yesterday Masters had me to lunch—not at a restaurant but at his club, very big league. He has been avoiding his club in recent months. A man on the skids thinks everybody knows about it.

He had on one of these new synthetic summer suits, a gold tie, and looked the picture of prosperity.

"Well, well, well!" he said. "I had your old elevator man up, as you suggested."

"He's *your* old elevator man."

"Well, you know what I mean," said Masters. "His name is Fred. I gave him a cigar. I suggested that he knew more people in our building than anybody else, and so forth. And in no time at all, I was telling the old boy all my troubles. I even told him I was slated to be fired in six months.''

''So?''

''About our customers, first,'' exclaimed Masters, leaning excitedly toward me. ''Fred said they were impatient and irritated because my front girls are too nice.''

''Too nice?''

''They are so ladylike, they feel they must hold a social conversation with everybody,'' explained Masters. ''He likes my girls, you understand. They are all friends of his. But he says they are too nice and ladylike for modern business. So he reminded me that I have two old battle-axes back in the filing and records department of the office. Move them, said Fred, up to meet the customers and move the pleasant girls back into the filing.''

''And you did?''

''And the switchboard!'' cried Masters. ''Our old switchboard girl knows every customer the minute she hears their voices. She is friendly with them all. She has been a regular institution around our place all these years.''

''I don't know a nicer switchboard girl,'' I agreed.

''But Fred said,'' hissed Masters, ''that her switchboard is probably all red while she is having cozy chats with all the customers who call in. I gave her a new assistant three months ago, a sweet young thing likely to develop under Lucy's guidance into another Lucy. But as you know, the switchboard is worse then ever. Crowded all the time.''

''So what did Fred say?''

''Pension Lucy,'' replied Masters. ''Fire the young one. And hire Fred's niece, a cold, practical girl about thirty, thirty-five.''

''Ah, his niece?''

''I hired her the next Monday. But what's more. Fred told me there were a couple of men in our office—accountants, they are—who haven't so much as exchanged a civil word with him all the years they have been in our organization. Mean, stiff characters. Fred said: Move these two guys up front to deal with the customers, and put all our pleasant bright young fellows back in the accounting.''

''And you did?''

''It was a riot for a couple of days,'' said Masters ''but then it settled down. It has been running like a dream ever since. Fred says there is far too much malarkey, too much making friends and influencing people, these days. Canada is getting to be big. People haven't time to blather over the counter, like in a country store any more.''

"So you're O.K. then?''

Masters held both thumbs up and beamed at me.

"I offered Fred,'' he said, "a job sitting at a desk just inside our door, to sort of direct traffic and keep things moving. But he turned me down. He said he had the most interesting job in the world.''

The Shoplifter

WHAT caught my eye and shocked it like an electric jolt was the yellow-and-gray silk kerchief.

My eye was on it, then it vanished.

I was in a big department store poking around the scarf and silk-square counters during these February sales, looking for a nice thick silk neckerchief to wear as a scarf. It was a yellow one I wanted, a nice lacey, touty sort of yellow.

Across the counter, which was a rectangle of bins in which the bargains were tumbled together, I pinned my eye on this yellow-and-gray one, good and gaudy.

A woman was fingering it as I looked. I started around the rectangle, keeping my eyes on it. Then, before my very eyes, it simply vanished. The woman lifted her hand from it. It was gone.

I halted. I raised my gaze to the woman. She was quite well dressed but housewifely. She wore glasses. As my eyes met hers, I detected a queer, tiny glint in them. She turned and walked away.

I hurried around the squared counters and tossed aside the kerchiefs where the yellow one had been. Not a trace of it. It was there in full view one instant. The next, it was gone.

I turned and glanced after the woman. My heart skipped a beat when I saw her standing 50 feet away, at a glove counter. And when my eyes picked her up, she was unquestionably looking at me. She quickly averted her gaze and walked away.

By the Lord Harry, after all these years as a newspaper Hawkshaw, I had seen a shoplifter for the first time!

To the book department, where the woman manager is a friend of mine, was less than 60 paces. I asked her if I could leave my hat and coat while I shopped. Coatless and hatless, I hurried around the far end of the gloves, hosiery and handkerchief department to the main corridor where the elevators are situated. I stood as though waiting for the elevator and surveyed the crowd of shoppers, nearly all women. I was watching for a brass-colored velvet hat surmounting a housewifely face with glasses, a gray cloth coat and a striped paper shopping bag.

She had not gone far. I spotted the odd light brown hat not 50 feet distant. She was turning over children's tuques and bright knitted mittens. Circling wide, I came behind her and, at the next counter, pretending to look at women's purses, I watched her. When she wandered away from the children's knitted things, I casually followed.

Her next stop was at an outpost of the notions department, where a cluttered counter displayed tea cozies, pincushions, dress shields, oven mitts, pot lifters, knick-knacks of every kind. My gaze never left her hands. She picked up a pair of black dress shields. When she set them down, they vanished! I saw her set them down. But when her hand moved away, the dress shields were not there. It was more than uncanny.

Over to the escalator she sauntered. I got in sixth behind her. We came out in the towels, washcloths, table mats and doilies. From 15 feet away, I saw her pick up a pretty mauve terry cloth washcloth worth forty cents. She looked at it. She set it down. But it was not there when her hand moved away! The instant she moved, she looked up square into my amazed eyes.

She smiled. A more brazen smile I never saw. She neither blushed nor turned pale. Walking off, she glanced over her shoulder. I was following.

Now I realized what was up. Her gray coat sleeves were wide. She had an elastic up her sleeve, to the end of which some sort of clip was fastened. When she picked an article up, she nipped the clip on to it. Extending her hand to set the article down, she let go the clip, and the article was snatched up her sleeve.

I followed. She did not hurry. I encountered a group manager whom I knew, in the blankets.

"Come with me" I hissed. "That woman there, in the light brown hat...!"

And I told him what I had seen.

The group manager spoke to a clerk. A store detective, who looked like a dear old farmer in town for the day, after selling 10 head of cattle, and downtown for a little spending spree, met us at the next escalator.

On my say-so, he addressed the lady in the brass velvet hat and asked her to accompany us to the private offices on the fourth floor.

She came meekly. She avoided my eyes as long as she could. Then she met them frankly, and gave me another cute little smile.

In the administrative offices, the store detective and my friend the blanket manager were politely dismissed. The shoplifter and I were discreetly admitted into the office of a gentleman known as the head of the store's protective service. The shoplifter sat down easily, and from her sleeve produced my yellow-and-gray scarf, four pairs of silk hose, a pair of black dress shields, a beaded silver purse, a tiny pair of child's colored mittens and a mauve wash cloth.

"Mr. Clark," said the head of the store's protective service, "I regret to have to tell you that you have succeeded in pinching part of our protective service. This is Mrs. Archer. Her job is to test our own protective staff as well as the watchfulness of sales people."

"You mean...?" I mumbled.

"Yes, she is a detective of detectives. She works one day in one department, and that night we check all her pinches and raise heck with the clerks and store detectives who failed to spot her. The bigger her loot, the better."

"Don't they get to know her?" I protested.

"Oh, she only works a month with us. Then she goes on to some other store, or some other city. Now and then, of course," apologized the head of the protective staff, "the employees get on to her through the good offices of some of our customers..."

"Ahem!" I said, rising. "Ho-hum! Hmmmm!"

And I sneaked back to the book department and retrieved my hat and coat.

(Incidentally, I got the yellow-and-gray kerchief all right, $1.59.)

The Tree

G ET OVER HERE," rasped the gravelly voice of Dandy Daniels on the phone, "as fast as you know how!"

"Well, just a minute, Dandy," I replied, "I was planning..."

"Stop fiddle-diddlin'," commanded Dandy, "and hop in your car and get over here. And bring that bucksaw of yours."

"Bucksaw? Dandy, I have no bucksaw," I evaded.

"That yellow-handed saw?" yelled Dandy.

And hung up with a bang.

So I went up to the attic where I keep my camping and fishing junk and got out the Swede saw, a little 24-inch D-shaped saw I carry up under the bow of my canoe. Very handy for firewood, clearing deadfalls off portages and that sort of thing.

"Where are you going?" asked my wife.

"Over to Dandy's," I said.

"I thought you...," began my wife.

"So did I," I admitted. "But the old boy sounded urgent."

Dandy Daniels always sounds urgent. Away up in his eighties, Dandy is as full of life and ginger as an eight-year-old boy. And in as much trouble. He lives in his old-fashioned and very trim little house with Hortense, his aged housekeeper, whom he treats like a slave. Now that I come to think of it, who doesn't he treat like a slave?

Hortense was standing on the top step when I pulled up in my car.

"There's going to be trouble," she announced, stuffing the plug of her hearing aid in her ear.

"What is it? I asked.

"That tree again," said Hortense. "He's going to chop off the branches on our side."

Hortense led me hurriedly through the house to the back door.

There was Dandy struggling with excessive energy and loud grunts with his extension ladder which he was erecting to rest against the branches of a poplar tree.

On the far side of the fence, Mr. Simpson, his next-door neighbor to the south; Mrs. Simpson, Mrs. Simpson's brother Joe, who lives with them, and the three Simpson children were standing in a group watching.

"Here, here, Dandy!" I exclaimed, hurrying down the back steps. "You've no business heaving that ladder around."

"Ah," said Dandy. "I see you brought the bucksaw."

I set the yellow saw down on the ground and took the ladder away from him.

"Now," I said, "where do you want it?"

"Mister," said Mr. Simpson, "if you lay so much as a hand on one of them branches, I will have the law on you and him both."

I rested the ladder against the heaviest branch and faced the Simpsons. They were standing close together, a clump, and their faces were pale and set.

"Now what is this?" I inquired.

"That," said Mr. Simpson, as if making a speech, "is my tree. It grows here, like you can see, on my side of the fence. It is a Carolina poplar, planted by my late father, Albert H. Simpson, 20 years ago."

"And," said Dandy, standing back and striking an attitude like Sir John A.'s statue, "the damn' thing has grown like a weed. It is trespassing on my property. Its branches stick away out over my yard, so not a thing will grow in those garden borders there. And nothing but green moss on what ought to be the lawn under it."

"It's a beautiful tree," said Mr. Simpson loudly, glancing to see if any of the neighbors were leaning out their windows, "one of the finest trees in this whole neighborhood, and it has took a lifetime to grow."

"All I intend to do," enunciated Dandy, equally oratorically, "is lop off the branches that trespass over my side of the fence. The roots of that tree, which is no more than a weed, as any tree man will tell you, are crawling all through my drains."

"If," said Mr. Simpson, his family drawing closer around him, "you cut the branches, you will disfigure and mutilate the tree."

"It dumps," said Dandy, "two tons of leaves into MY garden every fall."

He picked the yellow saw off the ground.

"Hold the ladder steady," he commanded.

"I warn you!" cried Mr. Simpson, whose wife had hold of his elbow and was giving it jerks.

With saw in hand, Dandy stepped on the bottom rung of the ladder, and I went around to hold it steady against the branch above.

"You TOUCH that tree," shouted Mr. Simpson, "and I call the police!"

"Good!" said Dandy, mounting to the second and third rung. "And they'll tell you you can't let your trees go trespassing on other people's property."

Dandy mounted to the fourth rung and flourished the Swede saw.

"What's more," said Dandy, "I'll see if the police will lay a charge of theft against you."

"Theft!" said Mr. Simpson.

"This tree," said Dandy, mounting to the fifth rung and laying hold of the lowest branch, "has been stealing nourishment out of my soil all these years."

"Many's the time," cried Mrs. Simpson, joining the battle, "I've seen YOU sitting in its shade on hot days of summer and looking mighty grateful."

Dandy cautiously mounted to the sixth rung, raised the saw and laid it against the lowest and fattest branch.

"Sorry," he said, "but us property owners have to watch out for our private interests. This tree shades my land so nothing will grow, not even the grass."

He drew back his arm for the first stroke of the saw.

"Listen! Mr. Daniels!" said Mr. Simpson, stepping forward and laying hold of the top of the fence. "Will you consider a deal? I'll make you a deal. If I undertake to look after your garden? If I get Roy here to cut your grass regular, and I'll get some of that special grass seed that grows under trees and in sandy places, and if I get some begonias and things that will do all right in these beds here under the tree...?"

Roy, the oldest of the Simpson children, a boy of 13 or so, drooping, turned aside and was muttering beneath his breath.

Old Dandy lowered his arm with the saw.

"Well, now," he said, heartily, "that's something worth considering."

"Roy will cut your grass, front and back," went on Mr. Simpson, "regular."

Roy was walking toward the Simpsons' back door.

"Begonias, you say?" said Dandy, aloft. "You mean those bright-colored tuberous begonias, with the big blooms?''

"They do wonderful in the shade," enthused Mrs. Simpson.

"And," said Dandy, descending two rungs, "how about this sour moss that's growing here under the...?"

"I'll get some garden lime," said Mr. Simpson, "and some special fertilizer they got for this kind of thing..."

Dandy came down all the way and handed me my yellow saw.

"Very well," said he. "You take care of the injury your tree does to my premises, plus the service of your boy to keep my lawns cut. Lawns, I said. Plural."

"Mr. Daniels," said Simpson, warmly. "Shake!"

And he actually shook hands with old Dandy.

When we had carried the ladder back down to the cellar and Hortense was getting us a pot of tea, Dandy sank back in his favorite chair with a large sigh.

"You old rascal!" I said.

"I did it for Hortense," said Dandy, piously. "She's getting too old to shove lawn mowers any more."

He looked very smug.

"Hortense!" he yelled, thumping on the floor with the big brass ash tray he keeps for the purpose of attracting her attention. "Get a wiggle on! Where's that tea?"

Fellow Passenger

ITS A LONG, long while from May to December. But to a fellow of my age, three days on the across-Canada train from Montreal to Vancouver, with Pete Mitchell, looked like an eternity.

As I hustled along the Montreal platform behind the redcap, early Monday afternoon, to catch The Canadian, who did I spy not 10 paces ahead of me but Pete Mitchell.

Here I had been looking forward, as only a newspaperman can, to three nights in my cozy private bedroom, and three cozy days with my typewriter on a little table, and a wide window to glance up out of between paragraphs, while hour by hour the broad Dominion wheeled by.

And here ahead of me, possibly heading for the same car, was Pete Mitchell, a distant kinsman of mine, with whom I went to high school and Varsity, my age exactly; and the doggonedest bore in the world. Member of the international of not one but two or three services clubs; red-hot pioneer of the old League of Nations Society, and now just as excited about the United Nations; director, if not worse, of half a dozen societies for the prevention of this and the control of that.

"Pssst!" I said to my redcap, tweaking his sleeve. And we slowed up.

We came to my car, and I was happy to see Pete waddling on. I hung back on the step and peeked until I saw him board the car ahead of mine.

Then I hustled into my bedroom, C; and when the redcap departed, I twitched on the door lock.

What a predicament! Imagine being trapped on a train with Pete! I pulled down the shade of the window for fear Pete might go for a last-minute promenade on the platform and detect me. He is always looking for audiences, even on station platforms. I sat back, before indulging in the pleasure of laying out my typewriter and disposing of my goods and chattels and magazines around the little room. I sat back and miseried.

By the time the train got started, I had decided on a plan of action. I did not intend to be cooped up a prisoner from Monday afternoon until Thursday morning.

I rang for the porter. He was a small man of about my own age, probably wise in the ways of the world. I made a clean breast of the matter to him.

"His initials," I told him, "are P.M., and they'll probably be on his baggage. The porter in the next car can locate him. Now, it will be worth $10 extra on your tip if you can get in cahoots with that other porter, and protect me. What I suggest is..."

And we arranged that he would keep an eye on Pete. And when Pete came back from the diner, and was either safe in his bedroom or back in the club car or up in the blister viewing the scenery, I could nip into the diner. And when Pete left the club car...

But above all, find out from the porter how far Pete was going. Maybe he was only going to Winnipeg or possibly Regina.

After a little while, my porter came back with a big conspiratorial smile and assured me all was fixed. The other porter would co-operate to the full.

So I relaxed, unpacked my goods and chattels, uncovered and set up my typewriter, laid out my magazines, took off my coat, lit up my pipe; and in some serenity of soul gazed happily out the window at the quiet tidy winter fields of Quebec, and knew that soon I would be seeing the wilderness.

My porter came in and announced that Mr. Mitchell was going to Vancouver.

"This," I said, "is going to be quite a trick, if we can pull it off."

"Count on me, sir," assured my porter. "Mr. Mitchell has just gone back to the club car. You can go forward, if you like, to the tourist club car, which also has a scenic dome."

And that is what I did, finding all sorts of congenial people up there to converse with.

Quite a bit after dark, my porter came to the dome and informed me that Mr. Mitchell had finished dinner and was again back in the club car, holding converse with several gentlemen, and that it was now safe for me in the diner.

Breakfast Tuesday was easy. I had it in my room. I was writing until mid-afternoon, when my porter came and told me Mr. Mitchell had retired to his room and was snoozing in his shirt sleeves. This gave me my turn in the club car, where I found a few interesting-looking passengers snoozing or reading and not much inclined to conversation. So I went up into the blister, my porter having assured me he would give me plenty of warning, via the other porter, when Pete woke up.

It was Tuesday night when we got to Winnipeg, and I would have liked to get out and promenade on the platform during the stop, but figured it was too risky. After all, there was all day Wednesday and Wednesday night to think of.

So I spent Wednesday viewing with tireless interest the vast wheeling plains of the prairies, on which, as my air-force son says, you can look in any direction for two days. From the crack under my window shade, I had a peep at Calgary. Thanks to the ingenuity and vigilance of my porter, I was able to visit the diner regularly without disaster, and had sundry interesting discussions with agreeable table mates. I also had two hours in the club-car blister, and another two hours in the forward blister of the tourist club car.

Besides, I got much more writing done than would probably have been possible if I had not been holed up in this fashion.

It was beautiful through the mountains, before dark fell vastly on them; and I was a happy man to wake on the down slope to Vancouver, which we reached Thursday morning. And I was so thankful, I thought it would be a whimsical and Christian thing, just as we got off the train, to encounter Pete, and be thunderstruck to see him, and marvel over the fact that in this whole wide passage of our beloved country, we had not known we were on the same train.

But as we filed off my car, I remembered I had left my walking stick back in my bedroom, hanging on the hook. I had already, I may say, paid off my porter, as agreed—$10 for all his sagacity, and $5 for his tip, AND, as a little special, $5 to give his friend, the porter of Mitchell's car, for his kind co-operation.

As I returned down the corridor, I heard the high, hilarious laughter and chatter of porters as they returned to the vestibule after seeing the last of their passengers off.

I heard my porter say:

"HE gave me $10 plus $5, AND $5 for YOU!"

Gay gales of laughter.

I halted and listened. After all, it is not eavesdropping to listen in the newspaper profession: it is in the public interest.

"Mitchell," gargled the other porter, "gave me $10 plus $5 for ME, and $5 for YOU, for your KIND co-operation!''

More howls.

I stood fast, assembling and sorting out my emotions.

''They're distant relatives,'' my porter said.

''Can't BEAR each other!'' yelped the other.

There was only one thing to do. I stalked around the corner, and with never a glance to right or left, marched between them and down the steps.

I could not see Mitchell ahead of me on the platform.

He had probably hurried away.

After all, it was no use trying to see him thunderstruck.

The Visit

THERE was a small chunky boy, about five years old, sitting on Miss Pitchett's doorstep.

I halted, I took a firmer grip on the book in my hand.

"Hi!" said the small boy.

"Hello, there," I responded cautiously.

I advanced slowly up the walk, rearranging my tactics. For this was wholly at variance with my expectations.

Miss Pitchett, with whom I was not acquainted, had telephoned me before lunch.

"Mr. Clark," she said, "our mutual friend, Mr. Gillis Purcell, tells me you have a copy of old Tiger Dunlop's *Statistical Sketches.*"

"Yes," I said, not without pride. "I have the 1832 edition, published by John Murray in London..."

"Oh, Mr. Clark," said Miss Pitchett, "My ancestors came out to Canada in 1835, and they bought their land in the Huron Tract directly from Dr. Dunlop, who was the superintendent of the Canada Company. Could I POSSIBLY borrow the little book?"

"Why, of course," I replied. "It is very fragile, you understand. A little paperback, 133 years old."

"I would take the greatest care of it," assured Miss Pitchett. "I live only four blocks over from you. I could drop by at your convenience."

I did some fast and fancy thinking. Miss Pitchett sounded elderly to me. And it has been my experience that elderly ladies, especially unmarried elderly ladies, who are interested in family history and genealogy are inclined to be long-winded: I didn't want to be stuck all afternoon with a long-winded lady.

"Why, Miss Pitchett," I said, "I go for my constitutional every afternoon. And if you live only four blocks away, I'll be delighted to drop the little book in to you."

"Thank you," exclaimed Miss Pitchett. "You can have no idea how I look forward to having this book in my hands. I have read everything about the old doctor, and own most of the books about him. But I have never laid eyes..."

"It's a delightful and humorous book," I cut in. "He was a wonderful old scalawag."

"My ancestors were terrified of him," said she.

"Indeed?" said I.

"They were teetotallers."

"Ah," said I.

So after lunch, I got down my copy of *Statistical Sketches Of Upper Canada,* which, on account of its fragility, I keep in a hard-cover slip case. I glanced through it, to refresh my mind with the old boy's hilarious descriptions of our pioneer cookery and our social customs of those gallant days. Then I set off for my walk.

And on Miss Pitchett's doorstep sat this chunky small boy.

"Hi!" he repeated, as I came slowly up the steps.

When I rang the bell, he stood up and studied the object in my hand closely. I shifted it to the other hand.

When Miss Pitchett opened the door, he stepped in ahead of me and vanished, to my relief, when Miss Pitchett insisted that I take off my hat and coat for a few minutes.

Her living room walls were stacked with books.

She took *Statistical Sketches* from me almost with reverence, and slid the slip case open.

"At last!" she said.

There was a loud clunk from back in the kitchen. It was a refrigerator door closing.

"He must be hungry," said Miss Pitchett, jumping up. "Excuse me a moment, and I'll get him something to eat."

"Ah," I said, taking *Statistical Sketches* back from her hand, "little boys are always hungry."

I could hear them chatting while I got up and studied Miss Pitchett's shelves. It was a good collection. She had all 32 volumes of the *Chronicles Of Canada* (I counted them). She had the same green-and-gold bound complete works of Francis Parkman that I own. She had 10 or more of the *Makers Of Canada.*

"I had no peanut butter," said Miss Pitchett, returning. "That's what he wanted. But I gave him what we used to call a 'piece' when I was young."

"I remember," I said giving her back the book. "Thick bread and butter, plastered with brown sugar!"

"Right," said Miss Pitchett, and we sat down to explore.

"I regret," I said, "that I can't leave the book with you Miss Pitchett. I remembered, after you phoned, that I had promised it to a young chap who is writing his Ph. D. thesis on the Canada Company."

There was a sound of dishes rattling in the kitchen. Miss Pitchett sat up anxiously and listened.

"I was hoping," she said, "to copy parts of it for my collection..."

"Well, perhaps some other time." I suggested.

The little boy appeared at the dining room entrance.

"I want another piece," he said.

"Of course," said Miss Pitchett, jumping up dutifully and accompanying the boy back to the kitchen.

I certainly was not going to leave *Statistical Sketches,* that fragile old treasure, in any house with any chunky small boys in it. The older the book, I recollected, the more a little boy thinks he should scribble in it, with pink or orange crayons preferred.

"Perhaps," I said, when Miss Pitchett returned and began leafing tenderly amid the old brittle pages, "maybe toward summer, you might come over to my place and spend an afternoon or two copying out what you want."

I figured by summer, this little boy might be off somewhere at a summer cottage with his parents.

"That would be splendid," said Miss Pitchett, glancing up as the little boy passed in the hallway and proceeded upstairs.

So for a while we two elders sat engrossed with the little book, I finding some specially witty and ludicrous passages for her, which I read to her with what I think is a Scottish accent, like the old doctor's. But Miss Pitchett could not pay full attention on account of various thumps and bangs coming through the ceiling.

"I had better," she said, "slip up and see what he is doing."

"Little boys," I assured her, "are always up to something."

So I had time to further inspect Miss Pitchett's shelves, and they were full of all the right stuff.

"He's made a sort of a den," said Miss Pitchett, returning a little breathless, "out of chairs and my bedside table."

"Small boys like dens," I explained. "Little girls play house."

"He's got the counterpane off my bed, for a roof."

So, a little regretfully, for that young scholar working on his Ph. D. was a sheer invention on my part, I stood up to say goodbye and put Dr. Dunlop in his slip case.

I could see Miss Pitchett was anxious to get back upstairs. The thumps and bangs were becoming a little more violent.

She helped me on with my coat and handed me my hat.

When I went to the door, she asked:

"Aren't you taking your little boy?"

"MY little boy!" I said, astonished.

"Isn't he yours?" she asked.

"My dear lady," I said, "he was sitting on the doorstep when I arrived, and he stepped in ahead of me when you..."

"Good gracious!" said Miss Pitchett, heading for the foot of the stairs.

"Boy?" she called up.

"BOY!" I called up, more masterfully.

He came to the top of the stairs, holding a small china figurine in his arms.

"I found a doll," he announced.

"Come down," I commanded.

Miss Pitchett took the figurine from him gently. It was Royal Doulton, the one of the girl in the windswept frock.

"Boy," I asked, "where do you live?"

"Up the street."

"How far up the street?"

"At the corner."

"Ah," said Miss Pitchett, "the apartment house. I THINK now I have noticed this little fellow playing about..."

We escorted him to the door. We watched him hippety-hopping down the walk and up the street.

"Miss Pitchett," I said, "I have been thinking. I do not believe this young friend of mine, the one who is working on his Ph. D. thesis, will require *Statistical Sketches* for a couple of weeks or so."

She took the slip case from my hand.

She understood perfectly.

"But," I added, "whenever you put it down, I wonder would you be good enough to put it up there, on one of the higher shelves?"

"Oh," cried Miss Pitchett, "you may be sure I won't let him in again!"

We shook hands and I left.
But I will spend a couple of uneasy weeks, just the same.
Little boys can do anything.

An Indignity

A TREMENDOUS new hotel opened in one of the larger American cities, and its management, as usual, invited newspapers far and wide to send representatives to do a little free-loading. I was elected to go, not so much for the free-loading, since I am a very small man and don't hold a great deal, but because it is good newspaper practice to have somebody on the staff who is familiar with all the fancier hangouts of the gentry. Besides, there would be sure to be many celebrities among the first-day guests, in some of whom might be stories.

When I drew up in my taxi from the airport in front of the magnificent new hotel, the grand admiral of a doorman courteously inquired if I had a reservation. And when he learned that I was one of the invited guests, I and my frowsy travelling bag were instantly put in charge of a young demigod of a bellhop who ushered me skillfully amid the thronged and fashionable lobby, got my reservation without delay, and shepherded me through masses of duchesses and millionaires into the gilded elevator and up to my room.

The room was fabulous. Modern, sleek, dazzling. Every gadget, including television. Two new novels on the bedside table. The bed cool and firm. The rug like a carpet of marshmallows.

I went into the bathroom. Perfect. Ivory tile, trimmed in sunrise orange. I turned to the basin and the mirror.

All I could see in the beautiful mirror, even when I stood on my tiptoes, was a little fringe of the hair on the top of my head.

There are no words to convey the indignation of short men who cannot see themselves in the bathroom mirror. It is a common enough experience. But we small men have learned to swallow our pride. To be indignant with dignity, you have to be six feet tall and weigh 200 pounds. All a small man does when he gives vent to indignation is to create a lot of mirth around him. So he burns up in secret; and when he

47

shaves, he has to keep walking back and forth from the basin in the bathroom to the mirror on the dresser in the other room. It's humiliating. But it is the better choice.

But worms do turn, in the most surprising fashion. I went to the ivory telephone and asked for the manager. Not the assistant manager, but the big-mogul manager whose name was signed to the warm and hospitable engraved invitation I still had in my pocket. His secretary explained to me how busy he was, on such a day, with all the famous guests arriving. But I assured her in the gravest terms that what I had to say to him was of the utmost importance to the hotel, to him and to me and all the other guests. So she put me through to him. I gave him my name, rank and number.

"Sir," I said, "have you got a city directory, one of those very big directories?"

"Yeeees," he admitted uneasily.

"Then please come to my room at once," I begged, "and have a bellboy bring the directory with you..."

"Er....uh...," he said; but he came. A tired, harried gentleman, with a rose in his lapel, and a bellboy behind him with a great big city directory.

I had the telephone directory from my bedside table in my hands when I opened the door to them—a good big book, too. I led them into the bathroom. On the floor I set the telephone directory, and instructed the bellboy to place his big directory on top of it. The manager was watching with a face stiff with impatience.

Facing the mirror, I stepped up on the pile of directories.

"*Now* I can see myself!" I said bitterly.

"Great heavens!" gasped the manager. "Mr. Clark, a thousand thanks...please excuse me...!"

And in utter consternation, he rushed from the room. I understand they instantly closed off one whole floor, while the contractors swarmed in and lowered the mirrors; and to that floor, the reception staff cleverly directed all the short guests for the remainder of the day and until such time as they could lower all the mirrors throughout the hotel.

At 6 p.m., I was moved to this floor that smelled faintly of quick-drying enamel; and the manager was there to greet me warmly.

"The architects," he said, "must have either been crazy or else six feet tall."

One or the other.

Surprise

THE SADDEST thing about Christmas, as we have it today, is that the element of surprise has pretty well gone out of it. We all know what we're getting for Christmas.

It would be better if some faint reflection of the surprise Mary felt, when Kaspar, Melchior and Balthazar strode in with their gifts, could show on all our faces this day.

Take the case of the diamond bar pin. My wife had reached the age, around about thirty, when she felt she was matronly enough to have a diamond bar pin. Costume jewelry is all very well for young married girls, but...

Along about November, she began her campaign. By Nov. 10, I was demanding to know how much a diamond bar pin would cost.

"I saw a beauty," she frankly confessed, naming the big jewelry store in town, "for $125."

"That's pretty steep for a working man," I muttered. "Tell you what I'll do: I'll look around and see if I can't get one a little nearer our budget."

"This one I saw..." began my wife, wistfully. But then she got up and walked into the kitchen.

Needless to say, I beetled straight next morning to the jewelry store, located the bar pin by its price, and by checking with the clerk as to whether a young matron had been in lately looking at that particular pin—a shy, dark young matron with the look of American Beauty roses...?

"That's the one," agreed the clerk, promising to swear he had sold the pin to a large, fat lady in case my wife came in again.

Then I launched MY campaign.

I went home and admitted that I had done a little looking around in the jewelry stores.

"My dear," I cried excitedly, "let's forget bar pins! Do you know what I saw today? I saw the most beautiful Ping vase..."

"Ping?" whispered my wife, pale.

"Chinese," I exulted. "You've heard of Ming china and ceramics? Priceless! Well, Ping is next to Ming, and I've located a vase, the loveliest thing you ever saw, a kind of glowing orange. I can get it for only a trifle more than we'd pay for a bar pin. And it will not only be a lovely ornament for the living room here, but will be an heirloom for us to pass on down to the children."

She went away to the kitchen to make some tea.

For two weeks before Christmas, I lugged home books on Chinese pottery and ceramics, illustrated, from the public library, and put on a wonderful act, reading her passages about Ming and Ping and Ding and several other fantasies. She was desolate.

Two days before Christmas, I went to the Five and Ten and bought the most outrageous vase they had, a ghastly orange, with purple warts on it. This I took to the jewelry store, where they were holding the diamond bar pin. And the clerk helped me arrange that the bar pin, in its cute little leather case, would be giftwrapped in tissue. Then it was to be stuffed, with a lot of tissue, into the vase. Then the vase was to be wrapped and sealed and ribboned. And finally, it was to be put in a large beautiful blue box, which again would be splendidly wrapped in tissue, with large ribbons, the color of American Beauty roses.

I never faced Christmas with greater excitement. Oh, surprise! Oh, Mary, Melchior, Kaspar, Balthazar!

Christmas morning, my wife and the children gathered in the usual pandemonium around the tree. There, at the back, was the beautiful imposing box with the Ping vase in it. I am clerk of the tree. I passed out the gifts, holding the Ping vase to near the last.

"Ah!" I cried, ceremoniously handing my wife the box, and standing over her to see her joy.

Off with trembling hands came the ribbons and the paper. Out came the vase. Off came its sealed tissue covering. There it stood, ghastly, emetic.

"Darling!" I breathed reverently. "Isn't it wonderful! Genuine Ping!"

I took it from her hands, tenderly, before she could start removing the stuffing of tissue within the vase. I went to the mantel. I lifted it piously. It appeared to slip from my grasp, and fell on the bricks of the fireplace, smashed to a hundred bits.

Even the children hushed their Christmas riot.

Here's where I did my act. I knelt down and began fumbling tragically amid the tissue paper that had been in the vase. A man can act far better with his back than with his front. I really put on a magnificent presentation of utter, speechless grief. I fumbled with the broken pieces and the paper, drawing it out as long as possible.

By golly, I couldn't find it!

The little leather box was not there!

The coldest chills I ever experienced began to flicker up and down my back. I frantically tore through the paper. I bent down and looked under the grate.

This was awful! AWFUL!

Finally, I had to turn and face my wife. I was forming the explanation in my mind, desperately, lamely...

My wife was sitting smiling luminously at me. Her dressing gown was drawn aside at the throat.

And on her nightgown glittered the bar pin.

"I always feel," she said, tenderly, "that there should be an element of surprise about Christmas."

Oh, Balthazar, Melchior, Kaspar, what can be done about these women!

The Spectacles

IT IS sometimes necessary to stoop to a little deception. Foster Hewitt, William Wallace (an advertising executive) and I had to go to New York City to put the sound track on a short commercial motion picture. We were accompanied by a couple of junior lads to whom a fling in New York would be a thrill.

Foster Hewitt's vibrant and exciting voice was to be used in the body of the film, and I was to mumble a short introduction and a brief finale, just to give a nice, homely, gravelly, cracker-barrel tone to the project, for the benefit of the up-country folks.

Of course, the first thing you do on arriving in New York on a business trip is to rush around trying to snag some theatre tickets. Both Foster and William Wallace knew New York far better than I, because I am strictly the fishing-tackle shop type, and am mostly familiar with what you might call the wrong side of the railway tracks. As the result of some pretty fast footwork and the help of some influential friends, Hewitt and Wallace came up with four tickets to the biggest and best musical revue in town.

"Now, Greg," they said, gently, "these young guys with us are just dying to see this show. And we figure you are more interested in Carnegie Hall and that sort of thing, rather than girl shows. We only got four tickets...er...um..."

"Well?" I asked, bitterly.

"We could try to get you a ticket to a big cello recital tonight," urged Foster.

I took the tickets from William Wallace's hand. They were in row ZZ, which is one row behind the last row, a cute little device they have thought up in New York. I handed them back, and turned away sadly from my friends and colleagues.

I went out to the corner of Fifth Avenue and 42nd Street and thought. I thought and thought.

53

Then I went along to Kresge's, and down to the basement. There they sell a great variety of eyeglasses, including some very powerful ones that magnify your eyes enormously, for the use of people with extremely short sight.

I bought the thickest pair, 79 cents.

Then I went to the theatre to which the boys were going that night, row ZZ. I got in the queue at the ticket office. Just before my turn came, I put the thick spectacles on, turned up my coat collar, set my hat very prim in the middle of the top of my head.

The face greeting me through the little wicket was the usual New York ticket-wicket face, grim, ice cold, rocky, hostile, with a cigar jutting out of its molars. I could see only dimly.

"Have you got," I asked huskily and meekly, "something fairly close up, for tonight? I don't see too good..."

The heartless monster in the wicket stared at me a long moment. He took the cigar out of his molars and spoke to somebody else, whose head swam into view. The two of them looked at me. Imagine a guy wanting to go to a smashing musical revue, a girl show, with eyes like that, big as quarters?

"Okay, buddy," said the ticket man, humbly. "Six sixty!"

And he tossed me a ticket for row A, right smack in the middle.

I had dinner with my friends and colleagues that evening; accompanied them sadly to the theatre; saw them safely in.

Then, just before the theatre lights went out, I strolled in myself, taking care to be seen by them, nodding very friendly to them, there in ZZ; and slowly, elegantly, as becomes a bon vivant, a man about town, and a very sneaky party altogether, ambled down to the bald-headed row.

Tangled Web

O UR NEIGHBOR, Mrs. Richardson, came to the door. "I hate to
bother you people," she said. "But I wonder if you would mind
if I sent my husband's Christmas present here from the store? I
want to surprise him. And he's bound to see it around the house."

"Why, sure!" we cried, happy to be involved in the merry mysteries
of Christmas. "What is it?"

"It's a new TV," said Mrs. Richardson. "We've had the old one for
seven years, and it's all out of date. I hate to impose on you with so big a
thing."

"We've lots of room," assured my wife.

"Jim is so devoted to TV," said Mrs. Richardson. "And of course I
love it too. But this old one of ours! Well, we're missing half the good
shows."

"We'll be happy to hide it for you," I said.

"I'll arrange to pick it up late Christmas Eve," said Mrs. Richardson.
"It ought to be up tomorrow."

"Righto!" said we.

And the new TV, a huge thing, all done up in a giant carton, arrived
next day, and we put it in the back hall, back of the ironer.

"Man!" I said, when my wife showed me it when I got home. "The
Richardsons are sure good to each other!"

"Well, they have no children," explained my wife. "They have
nobody else to make Christmas for."

It was about 9 p.m. when who should come to the front door but Jim
Richardson.

"Well, well, well!" said I, letting Jim in, and giving my wife a
warning wink.

"Do you folks," asked Jim, craftily, "mind doing a special favor for
a neighbor?"

"Name it," I said.

"It's my wife's Christmas present," said Richardson. "I've bought her a mink cape."

"Whee!" said my wife.

"And I know if I bring it home," said Richardson, "or send it up, she's certain to find it. And spoil the whole surprise. So, if you..."

"Why, we'll be delighted!" said my wife. "Will we be allowed to peek at it?"

"I'll drop over one evening," said Richardson, "and we can open it up and have a look at it. It's a beauty. It cost $600. But the poor girl has been going around in an old fur coat for five or six years. And I can tell, from the way she looks at these little capes all her friends are wearing, that she's just dying for one."

"Righto!" said we.

"I'll sneak over Christmas Eve and pick it up," said Richardson.

The mink cape arrived, in a handsome purple box, next morning, and my wife, resolutely refraining from having a peek, hid it in her upstairs closet.

Just before supper time, as we were about to sit down, Richardson rang our front bell.

"Hey, just a minute, folks," he said, entering. "I'm slipping in on my way home to ask, Did Ethel send a TV set up to you to keep?"

"Well, uh..." said I.

"A TV set?" asked my wife with great surprise.

"Oh, it's all right," said Richardson. "I know she sent it. I inquired from the manager of the department in the store we do all our shopping. And he admitted she had chosen a TV, and sent it in care of you."

"Well, now..." I temporized.

"I think," said Richardson, "she's selected the wrong one. I want to just have a squint at it. And if it is the wrong model, I can have them send up another one, and exchange it for the one that's here."

"Er...um..." I said.

I took Richardson into the back hall. We undid the carton enough for Richardson to see the front of the TV and the controls.

"Yep," he said, "just as I feared. She's picked the wrong one. Look. Is it any trouble if I have them send up another one, and they can take this away?"

"Not at all," said we. "Not at all!"

"And in case you see Ethel," said Richardson, "not a word, eh?"

"Mum's the word," we agreed.

And he hustled off home to supper.

Two mornings later (that was last Saturday) who do you suppose came to our door but Mrs. Richardson.

"Jim," she said, nipping in the door out of the cold, "has gone to the office to clean up some work left over. So I've come to have a look at the mink."

"The what?" exclaimed my wife and I.

"Aw, it's all right!" laughed Mrs. Richardson. "I know all about it. I picked it."

"You what?"

"I suspected Jim was getting me a mink cape," said Mrs. Richardson. "So I got the switchboard girl at his office to keep track of any calls he might make to any fur dealers. She tipped me off which dealer he was phoning. So I went to the fur shop, and the manager and I picked out this lovely cape. And when Jim called in, the manager just sold him the right one. It's easy for them, you know."

"But, Mrs. Richardson..." I gasped.

"Oh, Jim hasn't the faintest suspicion," said Mrs. Richardson. "It's perfectly all right. All women do things like this. Where have you hidden it?"

And she turned delighted to my wife.

They went upstairs.

I could hear them exclaiming, and I knew they were in front of the long cheval glass in my wife's room.

Downstairs they came, Mrs. Richardson in the beautiful mink cape, gliding and pirouetting like a model, and my wife patting the fur.

There was a ring at the door.

"Heavens!" cried Mrs. Richardson, darting into the dining room, and vanishing into the kitchen.

It was the delivery men from the department store with the new big TV set, to exchange.

Mrs. Richardson, reassured that it was not her husband or anyone who might peak, came back in.

"What's this?" she exclaimed, as the men hoisted the big carton.

"It's one we ordered," I tried lamely.

But she had already looked at the ticket label.

"We got to pick one up," said the delivery men.

"I imagine," I said loudly, "they must have sent the wrong one."

"No," said the larger delivery man, who had no feeling whatever for the sweet mysteries of Christmas, "it ain't that. It seems the man heard we'd sent that other model. So he came in and picked this one we've brought."

"You mean," cried Mrs. Richardson, shocked, "that Jim has been here and SEEN...?"

She clutched the mink cape to her throat in indignation.

I nodded dumbly.

"Why," she said, "that sneak!"

So the boys took away the other set.

And Mrs. Richardson and my wife went back upstairs and hid the mink cape, and then Mrs. Richardson, looking very indignant, departed.

"I guess," said my wife, "Christmas is a funny business without any children."

Retribution

I REGRET to announce that I am going deaf in the upper register. No longer can I hear the flight note of the pine siskin; and half the warblers, especially those with high-pitched, sibilant songs, no more reveal themselves to me, and I have to catch them by the eye, now, a poor way for a bird watcher. We like to hear them first, in the trees, and then seek them out with the binoculars.

But I've had it coming to me. It is retribution for past sins, that's what it is.

The hawk's thin, piercing scream is finished for me now, forever, amen. I can hear the whippoorwill and the shouted call of the pileated woodpecker. But the gossipy voice of the gull is only a mutter; the mad wail of the loon I hear sometimes, and sometimes I think I hear it when my companions say it is merely noises in my head. Hah. That is some consolation. Maybe, as I grow deafer and deafer, I will hear in my imagination all the birds I want. Hermit and wood thrush, the carol of the rose-breasted, like a robin who has studied in Milan; and in the dawn, the tireless recitative of the brown thrasher; or, lordliest of all, the deep command of the horned owl, stilling the dusk.

Well, heck, I should have known. I have it coming to me. It's retribution. You can't make fun of your hearing and get away with it. Fate is not a single goddess. Each of us has his own fate, perched on his shoulder, watching, slyly.

The time I offended was in July, 1940. We newspapermen who had been in the Retreat, or at Narvik, or who had witnessed the wild preparations in England for the expected landing of the enemy, were being called home to Canada. We had all taken an oath not to transmit, by cable, or letter, or by code, or any means whatsoever what we had seen of the collapse of the armies, other than what was released by censor. But we were full of news, full of immense detail that was of the profoundest interest and importance to our publishers. So they said:

"Come on home, tell us face to face, and then you can go back to Britain."

Which we did. And five of us managed to get berths on one of the C.P.R. Duchesses, from Liverpool, lucky fellows, with all those refugees, and those hundreds of children of name, taking up all the available space.

As we went through the embarkation sheds, carrying our bags and haversacks and bundles, we came to a barrier.

The British had set up a security block.

Even as early as July, 1940, the women of Britain were swarming to the colors. And at the barrier which we five had to pass, an elderly lady, an important lady, very intelligent, very commanding, was seated behind the long counter.

It has been my habit for years, when encountering an obstacle, to fall smartly to the rear. I got behind my four newspaper companions, and let them go first.

"Have you," asked the lady firmly, "any maps, photographs, phonograph records, cameras, film, either exposed or unexposed, or any documents, pamphlets or other printed material of military origin?"

Frederick Griffin was first in line.

"Well, madam," he said, "I am a war correspondent. These gentlemen are all war correspondents. I have some maps, and a few photographs..."

"Will you produce them, please?" cut in the lady, curtly. "We shall keep them until they have been passed by the proper authority, and they will then be forwarded to you in the usual channels."

"But, madam," protested Griffin. "We are war correspondents. We have taken an oath. We are on our honor. Anything we have..."

"Please open your luggage," commanded the lady, "and let my helper check your effects."

"But..."

"Do not delay the line-up!"

One by one, my four friends were interrogated, their baggage opened, maps, photographs, pamphlets—even pamphlets autographed by General McNaughton as souvenirs of these dread times—all were bundled up, with owner's name and address. Cameras were opened, films removed.

I had cameras, maps, photographs, even photographs I had got in the Retreat; I had phonograph records, especially of Albert And The Lion, and Sam Small's Musket. But it didn't matter; whatever they were, they were to be confiscated. I was in a panic. I am an honorable man. Also, I am an old soldier, of the first war and hold the King's commission. Am I likely to commit treason?

Boom! It was my turn next. I stepped smartly in front of the lady. My friends, past the barrier, awaited me morosely.

"Have you," said the lady, "camera, camera films, photographs...?"

I put my hand behind my ear and leaned forward with an eager and ingratiating smile.

"Pardon me, ma'am," I said, affecting the flat voice of the very deaf, "I'm a little hard of..."

"HAVE YOU," shouted the lady, "CAMERA, CAMERA FILM...?"

I hoisted my little Swiss portable typewriter up on the counter before her.

"No, ma'am," I declared emphatically. "It is NOT a camera. It is a typewriter. Everybody mistakes it for a..."

"HAVE YOU," cut in the lady, louder still, "any PHOTOGRAPHS, MAPS? M A P S!!!!"

Hand behind ear, and leaning farther forward, I struggled to hear her.

"No, no, ma'am!" I suddenly understood. "I assure you it IS a typewriter. Let me show you..."

I proceeded to open up the little machine.

"Everyone," I cried, "makes the same mistake. They are SURE it is some sort of camera."

"Oh, for Heaven's sake!" said the distracted lady.

She reached out and prevented me from opening the typewriter.

"Run along!" she commanded. "RUN ALONG!"

And she waved up the next person behind me.

I joined my friends. They were furious.

"You dirty little—!" hissed Griffin.

The others were equally frank.

"You'll pay for that, some day," declared Griffin. "You pretend to be deaf? You wait and see!"

I've waited.

Now I see.

How Christmas Came To Parliament Street

O N the 20-mile drive back to town from the suburban kennels where Wallace had bought this little cocker pup, I had it on my lap.

Is anything more utterly appealing, more lovable than a seven-week-old puppy? Especially, perhaps, a golden brown cocker spaniel puppy, with its long silky ears and its strangely seeking eyes—born blue, but already darkening and seeking. It cuddled in my arms, my warm hands. It looked up at me as it squirmed. Where was its mama?

"Look Wallace," I said, as we approached the city, "I would be glad to…"

"No, no!" cut in Wallace. "I've got it all set up with Mrs. Hamilton. She's in the next block from us. You're only six houses from us. Everybody in the block would know you had a new puppy…"

"I could keep it a secret," I pleaded.

"No, look," said Wallace, "Mrs. Hamilton has had cocker spaniels all her life. She's raised and trained a dozen in her life. Nobody would connect her with the Wallaces. And I want this as a surprise Christmas for *everybody* in our house—my wife even, and the older boys, but especially the twins. This puppy is *for* the twins, actually."

The Wallace twins are six years old, Ian and Alastair. The older boys are 11 and 14—a fine family.

"Don't you see?" said Wallace. "Early Christmas morning, I've got it all arranged with Mrs. Hamilton, I'll come around to her place. She is buying me a dog's sleeping basket with pad. And then I'll nip back to the house just as my wife and the kids are coming down to the Christmas tree. And in I'll come with Clan Wallace and set him down on the living room floor on his wobbly legs and big paws…"

"Clan Wallace?" I checked.

"Yes, that's the name I've decided on for him. It's a good name. Clan! Clan! Come here Clan!"

Wallace gloated.

"And the first thing he'll do," I said, "when you put him down, he'll piddle on the broadloom!"

"Don't worry," assured Wallace. "Old Mrs. Hamilton is coming over every day to show us how to housebreak a puppy; and it won't take long."

In a few minutes, we arrived at Mrs. Hamilton's. She was watching for us from her parlor window and her hungry arms were outstretched the minute she opened the door. I placed the tiny golden brown creature in her arms. It nestled straight to her. We went in to her kitchen and there we stood and admired Clan as, on wobbly legs, he explored the kitchen floor for a good place to piddle.

"This is a few days of great pleasure to me," said Mrs. Hamilton, "for I am too old now to start another spaniel. My last one, Muriel, died last summer, as you may know. Age 15."

Wallace let me off at my house around the block and drove home to explain to his wife and family that he and I had been out looking for a good Christmas tree. But had had no luck.

That would be about 4:30 p.m., just growing dusk.

At 6:15, black dark, Mrs. Hamilton called me on the phone. She was sobbing.

"Mr. Clark! The little puppy!"

"Yes?"

"It's lost," said Mrs Hamilton. "The grocery delivery boy came about 5:15. He must have left the side door open while I went into the other room to write the week's cheque. A few minutes later, I looked in the basket, and the puppy was gone. I ran all over the house, I ran out in the yard into the side drive, up and down the streets...Oh, Mr. Clark, that poor tiny thing, on a cold night like this..."

"I'll call Wallace and we'll be right over to help," I said, hastily.

Wallace was at my door in four minutes.

"Should we get your boys to come and help?" I suggested as we headed out.

"No, no," said Wallace, and in three minutes on the double we were down at Mrs. Hamilton's. We searched her yard, all the neighboring yards. I watched the street and the frozen gutters for any telltale signs of a little wanderer gone crushed in the Christmas traffic. At 8 o'clock, we gave up.

"What damn luck!" groaned Wallace.

"Look," I said, "We'll call the Humane Society. Maybe somebody has picked him up. Or the street cleaning department. They keep track of... uh... anything..."

"Don't *say* it!" cried Wallace, as he left me at my front door. "We'll make a door to door canvass tomorrow. Are you game?"

"Eight," I said, "A.M."

At 8, we were out. We rang the doorbells of all the houses east and west of Mrs. Hamilton for two blocks. We started up the short street that connects Mrs. Hamilton's with ours. Then we came to Miss McCabe's.

"Well," she said, "maybe I have something to help you, gentlemen. Last night about 5:30..."

"Tony, the man who cuts my grass in summer and does my garden and shovels my snow in winter..."

"Yesssss!" urged Wallace and I together.

"Well, now don't rush me," said Miss McCabe. "I was sitting at my front window here, watching Tony shovelling the slush off my walk, to make sure he didn't throw any of that salt slush off the street onto my lawn..."

"Oh, for Pete's sake," cried Wallace. "Miss McCabe!"

"Well, anyway, I saw him suddenly throw his shovel down and run out into the street, waving his arms up at the headlights. And he picked something up. I thought it was a small cat. Or maybe a squirrel..."

"What did he *do* with it?" shouted Wallace, much to Miss McCabe's distress.

"He put it," she said primly, "inside the front of his coat, and picked up his shovel and waved at me goodbye."

"Now," I said, holding Wallace quiet, "where do we find this Tony?"

"Well, just a minute," she said, going to her buffet. "I have it here somewhere. He is a Russian, or a Pole, or one of these new Canadian people..."

It was a street downtown, off Parliament Street, a small undistinguished street in a very old part of the city.

We took a taxi, so as not to have to go hunting around.

We came to an old, tired house.

An old, tired woman answered our knock.

"Have you," we asked, "a man named Tony living here?"

"Yes, he's one of my roomers. What do you want?"

"Is he in? We are looking for a little dog. We think maybe he has picked it up."

She gave us a long, cold stare.

"Stay here," she said. "I'll get him."

Down the stairs came a strong, dark young man.

Slowly. The landlady behind him.

"Hello," said Wallace. "Do you know anything about a little puppy, a dog, about this big? Golden brown, with long ears?"

And with his hands, Wallace shaped a little dog about twice the size of a baked Idaho potato.

"I don't speak very good," said the young fellow.

"Miss McCabe told us to come here," said Wallace. "I paid $50 for this little dog..."

With a long stare at us, the man slowly turned and signalled us to follow him. It was a tired, old house. The stairs, the halls, were dim.

At the far end of the first floor the man halted at a door.

"I find heem," he said quietly, with a sort of desperation, "on street."

"Okay," said Wallace. "I paid $50 for him. I will give you a good reward."

"No," said the man, "reward."

He opened the door to us.

It was a cluttered, crowded room. There was a trunk in one corner. Suitcases stuffed under things. A cot. A bed. A hotplate against the far wall, on which something was simmering.

On the bed, against rumpled pillows, a small boy.

And in his arms, clutched, Clan Wallace.

Clan Wallace without a doubt! Squirming and wriggling joyously in the boy's arms, excited as pups are at the interesting world in which they find themselves, with people popping up in all directions.

Wallace went over and patted the pup, patted the boy.

Tony, dark, strong, young, heartbroken, stood in the doorway with me, watching.

"How old?" I whispered.

"Seex."

"His mother?"

"She died when he born."

"What's the matter with him?"

"Romantic fever."

66

"Since?"

"Last sommer."

"Doctors."

"Oh, doctors, doctors, doctors," said Tony. "Victoriam nurses come in every day. Lendlady downstairs come and play with heem."

"Is he going to be all right?"

"Oh yes," whispered Tony. "Doctors say when winter go past, I take heem out in park."

Wallace was down on one knee beside the bed, stroking the golden head of the pup. The boy, wide-eyed with fright, was clutching it to his breast.

"Clan," said Wallace. "That's his name. Can you call Clan?"

"Clan!" said the boy.

"If your father thinks you can keep him in this room," said Wallace, "you can have him." He got up and walked to us at the door, reaching into his hip wallet pocket. I don't know how much he gave Tony.

"This afternoon," said Wallace, "I will bring down a basket, with pad, for him to sleep in. And a friend of mine, Mrs. Hamilton, will come down with it; and come in from time to time to see him. She knows how to look after puppies."

"I know!" said Tony. "I not got feefty dollars!"

"No, no," said Wallace.

"My father farm," said Tony, "many, many dogs. Little dogs. Baby dogs. I know. My father farm near Praha."

"Praha?" I questioned.

"You call heem Prague," said Tony. When he closed the door after us, we could hear him run across the room. At the foot of the stairs was the grim old landlady, her hand on the banister post.

"Well?" she asked.

"Can they keep it up there?" asked Wallace.

"God bless you, man," said she, turning to hurry up the dark stairs.

On our way to Parliament Street to flag down a taxi, Wallace was pretty quiet.

"What's the matter with the boy?" he finally asked.

"Rheumatic fever," I said, "but he's getting better. Victorian nurses come in every day or so."

"Do you suppose they will let him keep the pup, in that shabby room?"

"That old battle-axe of a landlady will see they do." I said.

When we got into the cab, Wallace relaxed back and blew a heavy sigh.

"It is not often, nowadays," he said in a slightly thick voice, "that real Christmas comes to you."

The Dust

NORMALLY, I do not pick up strange female hitchhikers.

Indeed, I have made it a lifelong practice not to do so. I have been warned that it leads to all sorts of complications. And at my age, there are enough complications.

But this elderly lady, standing just at the corner of the highway where the gravel road turns west toward Perkins Landing, looked so forlorn and at the same time so indignant that I could not pass her by.

She was thumbing as Queen Victoria might have thumbed, if you can imagine such a thing.

And besides, my life-long principles hardly had time to assert themselves as I turned the car left off the highway and into the gravel road. I had to cut across less than eight feet from her. In a way, she commanded me to stop.

She was a neat, tidy old lady. Her white hair was frizzy, as only old-fashioned curling tongs, heated in an oil-lamp chimney, can make it. She had a black dress and a string of jet beads around her neck.

"Well!" she huffed, as I threw the far door open for her. "It's about time SOMEBODY stopped!"

Her squinty eyes were snappy as the surveyed me.

"May I give you a lift, ma'am?" I asked, correctly.

"You may," she replied, backing and crawling into the car seat as the elder generation does. "You can let me out at Perkins Landing."

"Yes, ma'am," said I.

"And," she announced, hitching herself around in the seat the way old ladies do, to get settled, "I am in a hurry."

"Yes, ma'am," I responded.

The gravel road into the Landing is pretty dusty at this time of year.

"Phew!" said the old lady, fanning herself, as we met a car that enveloped us in a swirling cloud. "Close that window."

"Yes, ma'am," I agreed hastily.

The road is rather rough, too. Seven miles of it.

"Phew!" said the old lady. "It's stifling. Open that window."

"Yes, ma'am," I assented.

A small panel truck came from behind, in my dust cloud, blew for a pass, and rushed past us, blinding us with its dust.

"For Heaven's sakes," cried the old lady. "Slow down. Let the dust settle."

"Yes'm," I abbreviated, suiting the action to the words.

"I don't want to get there," she declared, "plastered with dust, shaken to pieces and soaked in perspiration!"

"No'm," I submitted.

"And," she remarked, "don't you ever clean your windows?"

"I've come a long way, ma'am," I pleaded. "Grasshoppers, bees, dust..."

"I can hardly see out," she reproved.

Another car came from behind, easily overtaking us at the speed we were going. I drew over. It whooshed by in another storm of dust.

"For mercy's sakes!" she erupted. "Are you going to let every car on the road pour dust on us?"

I put on speed.

"Awfff!" she coughed. "But let the dust settle first. Close that window!"

I slowed to let the dust settle.

Another car gave a sharp toot, I swerved over and it rushed past in another tornado of dust and gravel.

The old lady twisted herself around so as to be able to stare at me.

"Now, listen!" she stated. "Open that window before I smother. And if you let another car pass us...!"

There was female menace in her voice.

"Do you hear me?" she demanded.

"Certainly, ma'am."

"There's a car coming now," she informed me. "DON'T let it pass."

I increased speed.

"And DON'T shake me to pieces!" she directed. "Just go at a decent speed, and KEEP in the middle of the road, so it can't pass. Let IT take OUR dust for a change. Simple, isn't it?"

The car was already on my tail. It was edging over to the left, and its horn blew.

I held the middle.

The horn blew very close under my tail.

I still held the middle. Indeed, I veered a trifle to the left too, to indicate I was not going to let it pass.

It blew a series of blasts, closer, closer, closer.

"Hang on!" commanded the old lady, grimly.

But the horn was now so furious under my left rear fender that I could not refrain from putting on a trifle more speed.

"Easy!" cried the old lady. "Easy. Don't race him."

Then I saw a car coming toward us. I knew I had to draw over to the right. And if I did not do so soon enough, the car right behind me, smothered in my dust, might not see it.

It was a frightening situation. I defied the old lady.

I drew over to the right.

The car behind leaped furiously past.

And to my horror I saw it was a black-and-white car with a tall radio antenna sticking up from the middle of its brow.

A police car.

The oncoming car passed.

The police car ahead of me was braking, braking.

I braked in behind it, in its dust cloud. It stopped. I stopped.

"Awwwfff! Phew! For Heaven's sakes!" cried the old lady, fanning herself.

Two provincials bailed out of their car, and came slowly back to us, hitching their belts and tipping their caps back off their foreheads.

They approached on either side.

The one on my side was gray with rage.

"Refusing the right of way," he said through his teeth. "Obstructing the police. Dangerous driving!"

"Why, hello, Grandma!" said the one in the other window.

"Charlie!" ordered the old lady, dusting at her dress with her hankie. "Drive behind us, and don't let anybody pass."

"Yes, Grandma!"

My cop bent down and peered across me.

"Oh, hello, Grandma!"

The two provincials went and got in their car and waited until I drew past. They followed at a respectful distance all the way to Perkins Landing, where I let the old lady out.

Nobody else passed us.

Dog Gone

WHERE," yelped my aged friend Dandy Daniels over the phone, "can I get hold of a good howling dog?"

"Good heavens, Dandy!" was all I could say. For Dandy, who is away over 80, is the last man on earth I would in any way associate with a dog, even a small quiet dog.

"A howling, yowling dog," repeated Dandy malignantly. "A barking, yapping, snarling dog. A dog with a bass voice, or maybe one of these tenors. A rock 'n' roll dog. Yow-wow-wow! A yodelling dog..."

"Dandy, darlin'," I cut in, "take it easy! You'll strain yourself."

"I want you," said Dandy, "to pick me up and drive me to the dog pound."

"They don't have dog pounds any more, Dandy," I soothed him. "The Humane Society takes care of..."

"Drive me to the Humane Society, then," commanded Dandy. "And I'll get me a dog that will teach this neighborhood a thing or two."

"Aha!" I said.

For old Dandy is forever at war with his neighbors, on one count or another.

"Aha yourself!" snapped Dandy. "This whole district has gone nuts. You can't hear yourself think for dogs barking, howling, hooting and yapping. On the south side of me is a cocker spaniel that spends all day and half the night howling to be let in. On the north side, there's this big black mutt that sounds like a freighter signalling to pass to starboard— hoot, hoot!"

"Now, now, Dandy..."

"In this one block," yelled Dandy, "there are 14 dogs. Count 'em. Big dogs, little dogs, medium dogs. EVERYBODY's got a dog. You should see the procession of them making the rounds first thing every morning. Up and down the street, hoisting their hind legs..."

"Now you be careful, Dandy," I warned. "No more catapults!"

Some years ago, Dandy was caught in the act of shooting at dogs trespassing on his property with a catapult from his upstairs window.

"Remember that police sergeant that caught you cold?" I reminded him.

"He's dead," said Dandy, comfortably. "I went to his funeral."

"Well, there's more of them," I warned.

"Listen," said Dandy. "If everybody can have dogs that yap and howl from 6 a.m. to past midnight, then I can have a dog, too. And I'm going to TRAIN it to start howling at 3 a.m...."

"Dandy, dear," I pleaded, "this is no time of year to have a dog. Think of the mud it will track into the house. Think of poor Hortense on her knees all day long mopping up mud..."

Hortense, who has been Dandy's housekeeper for 40 years, is as old as Dandy.

"Good exercise for her," said Dandy. "When do you pick me up?"

So I picked Dandy and Hortense up at 2 p.m. and drove them across town to the office and kennels of the Humane Society.

"I want," said Dandy to the man in the office, with all the gentle airs of a philanthropist, "to give a good home to a homeless dog. A problem dog, if you have one. One that howls."

The Humane Society man looked at us curiously.

"I'm afraid there isn't much in, today," he said. "But come and have a look."

In the kennels were half a dozen assorted dogs, most of them asleep from the weariness of whatever misadventures had brought them into the Humane Society's care.

"Look here!" exclaimed Dandy.

In an end kennel was a large, owlish dog inspecting us with his head on one side.

"What's he?" asked Dandy.

"Well," said the Humane Society man, "he's a problem, all right. We think he must have strayed into town from somewhere in the country."

"What breed is he?" asked Dandy, standing back.

"Part hound," guessed the Humane Society man, "part German shepherd, part boxer, part farm collie, maybe..."

Hortense had reached in and was scratching the big dog's ears. The dog immediately shoved his shoulder against the bars and waggled with pleasure. You could see that he and Hortense were friends on sight.

"Can he howl?" asked Dandy.

"Weeeelll," said the Humane Society man, "I suppose all dogs can howl when necessary. Why do you want a howler?"

"It's just a notion I have," said Dandy.

"What's his name?" asked Hortense, screwing in her ear plug.

"We have no idea," said the Humane Society man.

"I'll call him Dan," said Hortense, putting her arm through the bars and encircling the head of the big brute.

"Arrmmphhh!" said Dandy.

So we took him, after paying $2 for the license and tag, and a fee of $3 which the Humane Society man assessed as the value of the dog.

"We charge up to $10," he explained, "depending on the quality of the animal..."

"Five bucks!" said Dandy, thoughtfully, extracting the bill from his wallet with the two elastics around it.

Hortense had the big dog on a cord, but it pressed so close to her, and stared so eagerly up at her face that it was evident no leash was needed.

Dandy followed them out. The Humane Society man nodded to me to delay.

"As far as howling is concerned," he said, quietly, "we haven't heard a sound out of that dog since he came in. But he's a fighter."

"A fighter?"

"That's why we picked him up," said the Humane Society man. "We think he strayed in from the country somewhere. All he was looking for was fights. He is as tame as a rabbit with people. They'll love him. But the sight of a dog drives him crazy. In his passage through the streets where we picked him up, he drove every dog indoors..."

"I'll tell Mr. Daniels," I said.

But I didn't.

As we got out of the car at Dandy's, the big black dog next door south came bouncing around the corner to boom at us.

Dan, with never a sound, plunged out of the car. There was a blur of black and brown, a few wild, freighter-like toots from the black fellow, rather like a ship going down at sea. Then a wild chase down the side alley. A door slammed.

And Dan, sweet as a lamb, came trotting back, wagging his tail; lifted his big thick head to Hortense's hand, and was escorted into his new home.

"What did you think of that?" I asked Dandy.

"I'll teach him," said Dandy, "to sing."

It was 10 p.m. when Dandy phoned me.

"Hurrooo!" he yelled.

"How's things?" I enquired.

"They've got the police on me!" exulted Dandy.

"How?"

"Every time a dog so much as opens his yip," howled Dandy, "I let Dan out. He's got every dog in the district locked indoors."

"Well?"

"The whole neighborhood's up in arms," cried Dandy. "Deputations at my door. Telephone ringing so I can hardly get through to call you. And a police sergeant has just left."

"What did you say to him?"

"I just said," trumpeted Dandy, "that my dog didn't like to hear other dogs barking. So all he does is go out and stop 'em."

"What did the sergeant say?"

"He's gone away," said Dandy, "to think it over."

Signs

THE BUS in which I travel downtown and back has good, clear signs on its inside walls. "PLEASE LEAVE BY REAR EXIT."
They are beautiful signs, done in dark lettering with gilt edges. Prettier, politer signs you can't conceive. And they are bold, too. One is at the front, above and to the right of the driver, and you can't help but see it if you are seated in the bus, facing forward; or even if you are standing. The other sign is clearly painted half-way down the bus, in another strategic and conspicuous location.

Yet, by golly, at every bus stop, anywhere from two to five people always walk forward and insist on getting off at the front door.

Since everybody has to enter the bus by the front door, in order to pass the driver and pay their fare, this causes no end of delay and confusion. It has irritated me for months. How can people be so stupid?

It was raining and sleeting yesterday when I reached the bus stop, and three other people were ahead of me. The bus pulled up. It's door swung open.

Five people, taking their time about coming out into the rain and sleet, lumpily descended from the front door. I glared at them, but they weren't looking.

Getting on last, I took my stance beside the driver, holding on to the metal upright.

"Why the dickens," I inquired, "don't you make those people get off at the rear door, as the sign requests?"

The bus driver was a cheerful fellow, with a round face, his cap worn on the back of his head.

"Well, sir," he said, letting the bus in gear and starting, "it's really no use. I'd waste more time arguing with them than we lose by paying no attention."

"Can't they read?" I snorted.

The bus driver glanced around and saw the front seat beside me was empty.

"Sit down there," he suggested, "and just take a look at the types that get off the front door."

"They're types?"

"Sure are," said the driver, braking for the next stop.

Two men and a woman came forward to get off at the front, delaying four passengers boarding.

"See 'em?" checked the driver, as we proceeded. "They are mainly just stupid. Those three were stupids. But the next biggest type are the cranks. They take pleasure in going about defying signs and directions. They get a kick out of feeling bigger than signs. They like to go against the current."

Again we slacked to a stop. Only one person came up to the front, a man. After he had very deliberately descended, two passengers got on. We ground into motion again.

"What was he?" I inquired.

"Crank," said the driver. "Didn't you notice the way he sort of dawdled getting off, sort of daring anybody to object? He pushed his way off, making those waiting stand aside."

"I see," I saw.

"The cranks," reflected the driver, talking half over his shoulder confidentially, "I guess are what you call frustrated people. They've got maybe insignificant jobs, somewhere, and they've got to go around looking for little ways to assert themselves. The last type, you'll notice, are the nice, daffy people who just don't pay attention to signs or anything else—they're kind of in a swither all the time, or dreaming."

Next stop, two women came forward, laden with parcels. It was quite a moment before they could descend, and allow four to get on.

"The daffy type," mentioned the driver, as we proceeded. "Now, how could you train or educate such...?"

The driver suddenly lurched half to his feet, clutching the steering wheel. The big bus shuddered as he tramped on the brakes. The tires screeched, and there was a slight skid perceptible to us all as we were jolted and shaken.

I stood up as soon as I could, and over the driver's shoulder, I could see the car we had nearly collided with, stopped not a foot ahead of us across our bows.

The car slowly got in motion and out of our way. Our driver, with a great sigh, eased the bus gently into gear and slowly fed her gas.

"We used to have a sign right here." he said, "that read:
"PLEASE DO NOT TALK TO DRIVER."
"But nobody paid any attention to it. So we gave it up."
The bus gathered speed.

"Excuse me," I said politely, and went away back near the rear of the bus, handy to the exit, where I could get off properly, legally and with a sense of righteousness.

Moose Meat

W HEN you telephone B. J. Winter, his switchboard girl says:
"Who is speaking, please?"
"Clark," you say. "G. Clark."
"Just a moment, sir."
She then plugs you into B. J. Winter's secretary, who says, "Who is speaking, please?"
"Clark. G. Clark."
"What is it in connection with, please?"
Usually I just yell:
"None of your darn' business! Put me through to Mr. Winter or I'll..."
All this is bad enough. But when B. J. Winter telephones you, his secretary says, "Mr. Clark? Mr. Winter calling. Hold the line, please."
So you sit there, holding the thing to your ear while Mr. Winter's secretary goes and finds Mr. Winter, who by this time, being one of these 100-per-cent efficient businessmen, has hared off on some other wild spurt. And after about five minutes, Winter comes on the phone.
It is my custom now, whenever his secretary says, "Mr. Winter calling," to hang up immediately. And when, in a moment, she calls again and says, "We were cut off," I say:
"Cut off, my eye! I hung up! If you think I am going to sit here waiting upon Winter's convenience, you're crazy. If Winter wants to speak to me, you tell HIM to call me."
And bang! I hung up again.
And in a couple of minutes, Winter calls me.
I'm sorry, old man," he says crisply. But you can see he isn't sorry. He's just one of those high-gear businessmen who follows the most approved business practices designed for the comfort, convenience and profit of the party of the first part.
Two weeks ago Tuesday, Winter called me, with the usual rigamarole

of the secretary asking me to hold the line, etc., etc.

"Oh, sorry, Clark," said Winter. "I was calling you with regard to some moose meat Pete has sent down. It came by air express, and it's in dry ice."

"Good," said I.

I will tell you about Pete in a minute.

"There's one steak for you," said Winter. "Two steaks for us, and some chops. The air express is very expensive. It was $8 for the parcel. I figure your steak as one-fourth."

"I owe you $2," I said, promptly.

"Well," said Winter, "I figure we should keep these things on a businesslike basis, eh?"

"Correct," said I. "When can I come and pick up the steak."

"Tonight?" said Winter. "Around 8?"

"Correct," said I.

Pete is Winter's younger brother, and my friend. I know Winter because of Pete. See what I mean?

Pete is, you might say, the antithesis of Winter. He hates business so deeply that he has never held a job for more than a year. He is a wanderer, a sportsman, and a sweet, sweet guy. Right now, it seems he is up in the moose country somewhere. Probably driving a truck, temporarily.

I arrived at Winter's handsome ranch-style bungalow up in an exclusive suburb at about 8:10. I rang and rapped, but no one answered. Then I noticed a slip of paper pinned with a thumb tack to the frame of the ranch-type door:

Clark—

Sorry we have to be out. Steak on back window sill. Will settle re express later.

—B.J.W.

I went around to the back, and with matches searched all window sills. A neighbor, noticing my matches, came out and got me a flashlight. We searched in vain. No steak on any window sill.

Next morning, I called Winter and told him.

"What a pity," he said.

"Maybe some dog got it," I suggested, "or perhaps somebody called before me, saw the note, and went around and helped themselves."

"It could be," said Winter.

I waited. He said nothing.

"Didn't Pete," I inquired, "send you two steaks and some chops?"

"Ah, I see what you mean, old chap," said Winter. "But my wife and I have invited a number of friends to come in for a moose dinner. And there's just enough for that party."

So I wrote Pete, airmail, to the address Winter gave me, and thanked him for the steak but explained what had happened about the window sill and all.

Pete wrote back last Monday, airmail:

"...I am fresh out of moose meat, but will send you some wild geese one of these days."

This morning, by air express, $11, came a big parcel from Pete.

All done up with dry ice were three gorgeous Canada geese, plucked and drawn and singed and beautifully cased in plastic wrapping as only Pete can do it.

On one of the geese was a scrap of paper on which Pete had scrawled in big capital letters:

"For B.J."

I studied it thoughtfully.

"Is that," I asked my wife, "BJ or 86?"

"If it's 86," said my wife, "they've got the 6 turned around the wrong way."

"Eighty-six," I pondered. "For 86. I wonder what that could mean?"

And the more I thought of it, the more mysterious it grew.

"Eighty-six," I said. "What in the world did he mean by 86?"

So I have just written dear old Pete as follows:

"Dear Pete—

The magnificent Canada geese arrived air express this morning. What a wonderful gift! And done up so beautifully, as only a true sportsman like you could do them. My wife and I appreciate them more than we can say. We will have a great party on them and will think of you and toast you in the midst. By the way, one of the geese had a little scrap of paper on it with the figure 86 written on it. I couldn't figure out what it meant, but assume it was some notation of your own that got in the parcel accidentally. Will write you again after the party and give you a hearty description of the feast of roast wild geese with sage and onion, apples roasted around them in the pan, a bushel of sauerkraut and a peck of nippy turnips well touched by the frost."

By the time I get a letter back from Pete explaining that it was B.J. and not 86, the geese will be gone.

At my age, you've got to write me very clearly.
My vision is not exactly failing. But it plays tricks.

The Boost

PARKINSON and I were standing at our local bus stop, along with three or four others, when this stranger spoke to us.

"I feel sorry," he said, "for those ladies in that little shop across there."

He indicated the fancy-goods, greeting-card and china shop of the Misses Feemy.

"I guess everybody in the neighborhood does," agreed Parkinson, who speaks to strangers more readily than I. "They're on the wrong side of the street."

"Two friendlier ladies," said the stranger, "you'd never want to meet."

"They are great favorites," I stated, "with all the residents around here. But, as you say, Parkinson, they are on the wrong side. Hardly anybody bothers to cross over to that side."

As a matter of fact, the Misses Feemy's shop is one of the oldest in the two blocks of our shopping section. It was there before the drug store opened on the corner on this side; or the dry-cleaning establishment, the two grocers or the fruit store.

"It's a funny thing," said the stranger, "the way one side of the street in these uptown shopping sections seems to dominate."

"I've often wondered," admitted Parkinson, "how those two ladies make a living, come to think of it. You hardly ever see anybody go into their store."

"I go in, every now and then," I remarked, "just to sort of cheer them up."

"Same here," said Parkinson; and I noticed that two or three of the others in the group around the bus post were listening with friendly interest. I guess everybody feels the same about the Misses Feemy.

The bus came. And we filed aboard. Parkinson and I sat together near the back, and the stranger who had been talking to us took the seat right behind us so that he could lean forward.

"I've just been thinking," he said. "Tomorrow's Saturday, isn't it?" We agreed.

"If you gentlemen are game," he said, "we could put on a rather interesting demonstration. I'm only visiting in the neighborhood, but I could line up half a dozen people. I am sure each of you could stir up a few of the neighbors. And maybe each of them could get two or three apiece."

"What had you in mind?" I inquired.

"Well, you were saying," said the stranger, "that everybody in the district knows and likes these ladies. I remember an occasion on which a neighborhood like this turned out and staged a sort of benefit for a storekeeper in the same fix as these two. By common agreement, everybody in the neighborhood, on the one afternoon, called at the store. The result was a regular procession of customers. Nobody bought much. They just went in and bought some small thing. But the effect was astonishing."

"By Jove!" I said.

"For Pete's sake!" said Parkinson.

And we both twisted around to face the stranger.

What a witty, interesting face he had.

"Yes, sir," said he. "Scores of people who had never even looked at the store before had to come and see what all the excitement was about. Even passing traffic stopped, and people got out to see what all the people were doing, going in and out of the store, or standing looking in the window."

"Mister," I said, with the picture of the Misses Feemy's little shop, across the street back there, in my mind, "you've got a swell idea."

"It would be fun," he said. "And the curious part of it is, a gag like that really does a lot of good. That storekeeper I referred to was set back up in business by the one afternoon's performance on the part of a few friendly residents."

"Actually," said Parkinson, "all that is needed, for most stores, is to make people acquainted with them."

"Exactly!" said the stranger. "So what do you say? Tomorrow, Saturday, let's start the procession around 2 p.m."

"I'm free," I agreed at once. "How about you Parkinson?"

"I'll come over to your place tonight," said Parkinson enthusiastically, "and we'll sit at your phone and divide up the neighbors, the ones we each know best, and explain the little scheme to them.''

The stranger had to get off the bus. We shook hands warmly.

''I'll be there,'' he said. ''Maybe two or three times!''

''Better not tip off the Misses Feemy?'' I suggested.

''Right,'' said he. ''It will be more fun for them.''

It was fun. Parkinson came over around 8, and we took turns on the phone calling the folks we knew best around the district, especially the old residents.

Their response was enthusiastic. Everybody knows the Misses Feemy, and feels sorry not to have done more business with them, there, alone across on the other side...

''Call a couple more,'' we told each.

When on Saturday my wife and I turned the corner, around 1:45 p.m., we were delighted to see the run on the Misses Feemy had already begun.

Usually all the shopping trade is on the west side. But here up the east side of the street were at least a dozen people either coming from or going to the Feemy shop.

We greeted them friskily, and they greeted us with knowing smiles.

A conspiracy!

When we reached the shop, there were 10 people in it. The Misses Feemy, looking flushed, were frantically darting about, waiting on the customers.

''We'll come back later,'' I said to my wife, ''after we've done our shopping.''

So we crossed over and made the usual rounds of the usual shops. The Saturday afternoon routine.

As we came out of the fruit store, I noted that the crowd was larger at the Misses Feemy's, and three cars were parked on that side, a rather unusual circumstance.

Parkinson and his wife waved across to us as they emerged from the Misses Feemy's. In the drug store and the groceries, we encountered another dozen who exchanged knowing winks with us, or held up small packages done up in the well-known mauve wrapping paper employed by the Misses Feemy.

Even though we dawdled with our shopping, there was a bigger jam than ever across the street when we were through.

''I'd love,'' I said to my wife, ''to see that stranger who began all this."

"The Misses Feemy must be bewildered," said she.

So we walked our parcels home; and I came back alone around 5 p.m. to pay my visit to the Misses Feemy.

There were still 15 people in the shop. I had to stand quite a while at the door end before one of the Misses Feemy noticed me. The store looked cleaned out.

"Oh, Mr. Clark!" said one Miss Feemy, pushing me confidentially into a corner. "How wonderfully it worked!"

"How do you mean?"

"The sale was signed, sealed and delivered by 3:30," said Miss Feemy.

"The sale?"

"Why yes," said Miss Feemy, surprised. "My nephew was looking after it. My nephew, you know. The one who spoke to you about stirring up a lot of customers."

"Oh, him," I recollected.

"The big chain-store people who were going to buy us out at a measly price," said Miss Feemy, "were to be here to look at the shop at 2 p.m. Even by then, we had a crowd. Before my nephew got them to come up to his price, we had a regular Christmas crush."

"Your nephew," I asked. "Where's he from?"

"The country," explained Miss Feemy.

The Lesson

MY FAVORITES among the tens of thousands of the wise and witty words of the Lord of Montaigne are:

"As absurd stories can be told of me as of any man living."

And he proceeded, around 1550 A.D., to tell some, with the shrewd suggestion to us all that we freely reveal our own experiences of coming a cropper.

I got on the train at Liverpool, headed for London. My reservation was in the restaurant car.

In these English restaurant cars, there are tables for four along one side of the aisle, and cubicles for two along the other. Cozy little cubicles.

The gentleman who got the seat facing me in our little cozy cubicle was elderly. He had the familiar remote expression of eye to be met with in English railway carriages. But more than that, he had a sort of nimbus or aura of remoteness about him.

He was dressed in tweeds. His complexion was outdoorsy. His hands were working hands. I sized him up as a country gentleman, a squire. But if he were not that, he would be, I figured, perhaps the manager of a small factory, working on war materials. Or might he be a ship's captain? We were coming from Liverpool.

He had no newspaper to hide behind. So, to preserve the proper tradition of the English railway carriage, I took a book out of my overcoat pocket and proceeded to read it. I could feel the eyes of my elderly table mate shyly figuring me out, too.

He could, of course, see the CANADA on my shoulder badges. While not really elderly, I still had my white panaches over my ears; and I looked a little battered by the sun of Italy and North Africa. I was obviously too old to be a soldier. Yet I was in uniform.

When I had allowed him a good long look at me, I glanced up and caught his eye, smiled, and said it was a fine day. In a moment, we were in conversation.

One-sided conversation, that is. For my table companion spoke in a very mild voice. When I revealed that I was a war correspondent, I expected him to rise to the opportunity and ply me with questions all about the war. But he didn't. He seemed more interested in Canada. He asked a few shy questions about Canada and Canadians. He wondered if we did much publishing in Canada, apart from newspapers.

I have always found that you cannot really steer a conversation in an English railway carriage. Before I knew it, I was regaling my new acquaintance with a broad, generous outline of Canadian publishing, from which I slipped easily into a fine, learned, over-all survey of Canadian literature.

From Canadian literature, I moved naturally and gracefully into the field of American and English literature, expounding particularly upon the effects of these two upon Canadian literature and the Canadian mind.

My new friend was all ears and eyes. He would occasionally murmur "Indeed!" and now and then say "Yes?" or "Indeed?" again. I felt this was an excellent opportunity to impress upon a country squire, or the manager of a small war industry—or was it a ship's captain?—the importance of literature in time of war. And to do the nice thing, I warmly recommended to him the literature of his own beloved land, England; for, despite what anyone might say...

We arrived in London. My friend got off ahead of me. The station-master, in his plug hat and frock coat, was on the platform to meet him. The stationmaster, lifting his hat, accompanied my friend to the taxis.

"Who," I asked the stationmaster, after the cab drove off, "was that gentleman?"

"Mr. Masefield," said the stationmaster, "the Poet Laureate."

The Wrench

H ELLO!'' said Herriot. "Here's a good-looking wrench.''
"Ah,'' said I, uneasily.

Herriot looked at me sharply, suspiciously. We were in my garage. The trunk of my car was open. Herriot had been idly looking over the random, rusty collection of tools there.

The wrench was much more beautiful than any of the other junk.

"Is this...?'' demanded Herriot, gravely, holding it up.

"Well, now,'' I protested. "I've intended to take it back a dozen times. Dozens of times I've planned to go back that way, through Orangeville, and drop it in at the farm.''

"Why,'' accused Herriot, "that was three years ago. Three years!''

I remembered. It was just this time of year, and it was sleeting. We got a flat tire on a particularly lonely stretch of a back gravel road, away beyond Orangeville. We drew off the road, I recall, right beside a decayed old red brick church, with staggery, faded wooden driving sheds alongside it. Herriot and Cooper and I got out of the car and looked in disgust at the flabby flat. I got out the tools.

There was no tire wrench. There was no wrench at all: only a pair of pliers. And my tire nuts aren't the kind that will come loose with pliers. It was sleeting.

The only farmhouse in sight was just 100 yards or so up the road from the church. "I'll go,'' I said, "and borrow a tire wrench.''

"I'll come with you,'' said Herriot.

"You don't need to,'' I mentioned.

But Herriot never wanted to miss a thing.

We went through the sleet to the farmhouse, up a lane. A burr-draggled farm collie, tied at the side of the house, barked at us furiously. We rapped.

A tall, massive, dark woman opened the door slightly.

"Is your husband about?'' I asked.

91

"He is not."

"Could we borrow a tire wrench? We're stuck with a flat tire there, down the road."

"My husband has the truck away. I've no wrench."

She was huge, brooding woman, glum.

"Look—any kind of wrench," I begged. "Just to loosen the tire nuts."

"MY HUSBAND," stated the great dark woman, "doesn't care for me to lend things. Maybe if you went on to the next farm..."

"I assure you," I said, "we'll return it. Just a wrench of any kind..."

She opened the door wider and leaned out. She saw our car pulled off the side of the gravel, with Cooper in the sleet working at the nuts with the pliers.

She closed the door. In a moment she returned and handed out this beautiful big nickel-plated wrench.

"It's his new one," she said. "Got it through the mail order. You'll be sure?"

"Lady, absolutely," I said.

"He doesn't LIKE me lending his things," she repeated.

Back to the car we went, and it was quite a time getting the nuts off the old touring car (last touring model Ford ever made, I kept it 13 years).

We finally got the dang tire off, put the new one on, threw the old one in the back with Cooper, and we had driven 40 miles before Herriot remembered we had not returned the wrench. I guess it was the sleet.

"So," said Herriot, in my garage, three years later.

Well, Herriot loved life. And he loved drama, and tricks, and gags. This was his doing:

It had been a Saturday we had stopped at the farm.

So it was a Saturday when we three, Cooper, Herriot and I, in exactly the same clothes we had worn that other day—I in a red hunting cap, turtle-neck sweater under a brown canvas jacket, Herriot in his snug Grenfell jacket and beret—drove back up the long lone road away beyond Orangeville.

It was sleeting! We watched the road and came at last, without doubt, to the beat-up old red brick church and its tumbledown driving sheds.

There beyond it a hundred yards was the small gray farmhouse. We drove off to the side of the road.

Herriot and I got out and walked in the sleet to the lane and entered. An old dog, burr-draggled, but untied, came and barked hoarsely at us, followed us to the side door.

I rapped.

In a moment, the same massive, tall, gloomy woman opened the door slightly.

I held the wrench out to her.

"Thank you very much," I said politely.

And Herriot and I turned and walked away.

The woman uttered not a sound. She did not shut the door. Pretending to be speaking to each other, Herriot and I glanced over our shoulders at her. She was leaning out, staring in stark amazement back down the road, where our car, the same old Ford, was drawn off the gravel. Cooper was painstakingly going through the motions of finishing up a tire-change job.

"Beautiful! Beautiful!" said Herriot, as we turned out of the lane in the sleet onto the road.

"It is worth it," I said humbly.

The lonely big woman, wrench in her hand, was still at the open door of the farmhouse as we drove away.

The Bequest

W HEN OLD Mr. Gray died, he left $45,000, which is pretty darn' good for the foreman of a small printing establishment.

I have been accused of having had something to do with the extraordinary will Mr. Gray left for the distribution of his money. But I assure you I was as astonished as anybody.

To his three nieces and one nephew he left $2,000 cash each. But to Bert, his favorite nephew, he left not one red cent.

The balance of his estate was ordered kept by the trust company to accumulate for 10 years, then to be distributed to six well-known city missions where they take in homeless men. The money is to be used by the missions exclusively for the purchase of books "of a type," says the will, "that, in the opinion of the mission management, will be most likely to be read by the inmates."

For his nieces and nephews, this was a shocker. And especially for Bert. We all supposed that the old man would leave at least half of his money to Bert.

Bert got no cash. All he got was Mr. Gray's library.

"Why, Bert," I said, when he came to see me after the will was read, "you're not so badly off. That library is worth a good deal more than $2,000. I bet, if you are careful in picking a good dealer, you can realize at least $3,000 for those books."

"Aaaach," gritted Bert, "right in the will it says he directs me not to sell the books but to keep them and study them."

"It was his lifelong wish..." I began.

"I came to see," said Bert, "if you'd help me sell the damn' things. Do you want to buy any?"

"There are some items," I confessed, "that I could spare a couple of hundred for. But, to be perfectly honest, I think you will get a far better deal if you sell the library intact, as a whole, and not after some of the cream has been skimmed off."

95

"It was valued," said Bert, "at $2,500 when the trust company listed the estate."

"You'll get more than that," I assured him, "if you pick an honest book dealer."

"Can you beat it!" demanded Bert, hopelessly.

"Ah, Bert," I consoled him.

For, since childhood, Bert had been the apple of old Mr. Gray's eye. As a little boy, he went fishing with his old uncle; spent summers with him; his Christmas and birthday gifts were always 10 times more than the other children got. It was as if Bert were Mr. Gray's son.

He assumed charge of Bert's education, and set money aside for him to go to the university.

But Bert never passed his matriculation.

Worse than that, Bert became a bit of a problem. By the time he was 20, he was the black sheep of the entire family. Mr. Gray, on one occasion, spent $1,200 to get him out of a disgraceful scrape.

But that made no difference to Mr. Gray. He still lavished his affection on Bert, right up until his death.

And about all the response Bert gave him was to come pretty regularly to borrow money.

Mr. Gray's library, of course, was the explanation of my friendship for the old man. It was one of the finest libraries of Canadiana in the country. Gray had quit school at the age of 13 and got a job as a boy in a printing house. By the age of 30, he was one of the best-educated men I ever met. No university professor had a better knowledge of Canadian history, or had a greater command of the English language in conversation.

It was his dream that he would raise Bert to be a scholar, a B.A., an M.A., a Ph.D.

And it was for Bert that he collected this wonderful library.

Now Bert had it. Bert, whose sole interests, at 30 years of age himself, were wine, women and song.

Two weeks later, I telephoned Bert at his sister's, where he lives, and asked him when he would be ready to go with me to see some of the book dealers I knew.

"Oh, they're gone," said Bert. "I sold the lot last week..."

"Bert!" I protested. "How much did you get? Who did you..."

"I got $1,500, cash on the barrel head," said Bert.

"Aw, Bert, $1,500,...! Who got them?"

"I met a chap in the hotel," said Bert, "who knew about old books, and I took him up and he browsed through them, and then handed me $1,500 cash, and said take it or leave it. So naturally, I took it."

"Bert, you've been swindled. Who is he?"

"I don't know. Some fellow in the hotel. I think he comes from Chicago."

I hung up.

What a pitiable end to old Mr. Gray's lifelong dream.

This was about three months ago.

Last week, the trust company called Bert.

A man had come in to see them with a letter he had found in a copy of one of Ralph Connor's novels he had bought at a second-hand store.

It was a very odd letter.

It was addressed to Bert, in care of the trust company, and dated last Christmas Day.

"Dear Bert:

The doctors have just advised me that I very likely won't last out the year, so I am making my will. You recall how faithfully I have tried to interest you in the things that have interested and rejoiced me. But I never could make you read, never make you look at a book. Well, I am going to make you look at books at last. I am leaving you my library, with the proviso that you do not sell it. Among the books I have scattered the sum of $10,000 in bills of $500 and $100 denomination. I imagine when you find the first bill, you will begin a search, and so find this letter, which I am placing in a novel, which you are more likely to read than some others, a novel that gave me great pleasure when I was your age. Take care of yourself, Bert, and start reading before it is too late. How often have I told you there is boundless wealth in books?

Your fond and doting old Uncle."

The past week, I have been with Bert to every second-hand book store in town, and in neighboring towns.

We have found about 40 of Mr. Gray's books.

We have several of the dealers trying to trace where the bulk of them went.

But the chap Bert met in the hotel, who took them away in a station wagon, doubtless strewed them along the way as he headed for points south.

"That $1,500 he handed me," groaned Bert, "right in my sister's house, right in the cellar, where I had the books piled, he probably

97

picked out of the books, right before my eyes."

"You likely weren't watching."

"No," remembered Bert. "I was upstairs watching TV part of the time he was down there."

"Ah, well," I said.

Godsend

T HE WOMAN on the aisle seat in the bus immediately across from me had me irritated. She was fiddling in her large bulgy purse. She had been fiddling in it for at least 10 blocks.

Why don't women take time off at home to set their purses in order? What is this business of hoking, poking, groping and shovelling around in a purse every time they get in a public conveyance?

She was a smart, fashionably-dressed matron of a woman, the kind you don't usually see in buses. They ride in cars. But I suppose at this season of the year, with Christmas only a few weeks off, a car is a nuisance downtown. So they use the buses, along with us common people.

It's funny the things that get on your nerves as Christmas draws nigh. I wasn't the only one. The man sitting in the same seat with her, in by the window, was also bugged. I could see him staring down with slant eyes as she groped and probed and rearranged the tumbled contents of her capacious purse.

I was glad to see her snap the darned thing shut and get up and waggle and wobble her way up to the exit and get off when we arrived at the main shopping centre.

As she stood up, a folded piece of paper dropped on to her vacated seat. It was probably something she had dislodged in her purse-mining.

The man by the window did not happen to see it in time to call her. Probably he had no more inclination to call her than I had. What a woman! Let her lose her possessions.

I was looking at the fold of paper when the man by the window spotted it. He picked it up and unfolded it.

Now, he was a middle-aged man, a respectable gentleman with his hat fair in the middle of the top of his head. Obviously, he was either the vice-president of a large concern, or the president of a small concern, possibly a partner in a comfortable insurance agency. He too had the look of a man unaccustomed to riding with us proletarians in buses. Likely he also had left his car at home during the Christmas crush downtown.

I could not help but note that he seemed quite suddenly very interested in the small piece of paper. He drew it aside and glanced around to see if anyone was observing him. Of course, by the time he got around to me, I wasn't.

He took out his glasses and put them on, and studied the paper while holding it cautiously down by the window at his side.

I have seldom seen such an expression of excitement light up a man's face.

Quickly snatching the piece of paper into his overcoat pocket, he again glanced around to see if he was observed.

Confident that his actions were unnoticed, the man fairly expanded. An expression of joyous astonishment spread all over his face. He beamed, he gleamed, he glowed. A man finding $1,000 could hardly look more exalted.

By this time, as you can realize, I was tingling with suspicion and indignation. By what right had a man to pick up a piece of paper obviously dropped by accident by a lady? And what was on the paper? Was it a cheque for $1,000? Was it, perhaps, some incriminating piece of evidence that this man, so unctuous and respectable-looking, might hold for ransom, blackmailing an innocent woman to the tune of thousands?

Why, but for sheer chance, it might have been I who had picked up that bit of folded paper!

I thought, at first, I would step forward and speak to the bus driver and tell him what I had witnessed.

But has a bus driver the right to interrogate or detain his passengers?

Then I thought I would go past my bus stop and get off wherever this so-called gentleman got off, and call the first policeman.

While these things were passing through my mind, I could see that with every moment that passed, the man's pleased expression grew. It was as though a load had been lifted off him. He looked less like the partner in a prosperous small insurance business and more like a mining promoter.

Then he stood up to get off.

I followed.

Still uncertain what to do, but determined, at this Christmas season, to do the righteous and citizenly thing, and especially to find out what the Sam Hill was on that piece of paper, I glanced around, on descending from the bus, for a policeman. But we were down in that respectable warehouse district where policemen are never to be seen.

There was only one course left open: to follow the man to his den, and so identify him.

I think he must have caught a glimpse of me unawares and sensed my concern with him. As he crossed the street, he turned and glanced at me. I followed him along the dismal street, full of warehouses, insurance offices, chartered accountants' offices and millinery wholesalers' warehouses.

We had hardly gone 20 paces before he looked over his shoulder to see me hot on his trail.

Half-way along the block, he turned into one of those decayed buildings on the entrance to which are numerous bronze plaques as well as cheaper painted signs naming the tenants to be found within, up a rickety elevator hauled on clanking steel cables, or else up narrow steep stairs: the perfect setting for the sort of insurance-agency partner who would attempt to blackmail a comfortable matron whose only crime had been to grope publicly in her purse, block after block.

I halted in order to take note of the names on the bronze plaques. And there he stood, just inside the glass doors, staring down at me.

Before I could move, he shoved the door open.

"Are you following me?"

"I am," I said. "And I wish to know what you intend to do with that folded piece of paper, that document, that I saw you pick up from the bus seat when that lady rose..."

"It's a godsend!" exclaimed the man, coming down the steps and at the same time drawing from his overcoat pocket the very piece of paper in question.

"Look!" he cried, unfolding the paper and presenting it to my gaze. "I've been nearly crazy the past few days trying to draw up a Christmas list. And what happens? A woman drops hers, and it's got everything!"

And there it was:

Aunt Jennie—whistling tea kettle and 4 batteries for hearing aid.
Mary—½ doz. grapefruit spoons.
Young Ed.—dressing gown, gaudy, $9.95.
Ed—little carpenter plane to fix door and windows that stick.
Towser—new dog basket and pad.

Pinkie—cheque for $10 (post dated).

Mike—two canoe paddles, $8.

Carrie—one of those flowery teapots with electric plug in.

Gertrude—artificial flowers??? the ones she sent me last year??

English Christmas puddings for the Smarts, McLarens, Foxes & Reeves.

"Perfect!" cried he. "Fits me like a glove!"

"May I...uh..." I asked, "just copy it off?"

The Matched Pair

AT LUNCH yesterday, right across from us, an extremely homely girl sat at a table with one of the handsomest young men I have ever seen.

The contrast between them was so extraordinary that I called my companion Bill Milne's attention to them.

"Wow!" said Bill.

The girl had not a single attractive feature. Her face was lean and tight-stretched. She had level and conspicuous jawbones like sleigh runners; you know the kind? Her eyes were small, like raisins stuck in her forehead.

"Maybe," I suggested to Bill, "maybe she's got money."

For the young man was an Adonis. And he was obviously bewitched by his grotesque companion. Fingers laced, he leaned forward, wreathed in those daft smiles only true lovers can achieve. It was as if he were gently moaning all the time he gazed at her.

"No, not money," I corrected.

The girl's clothes, while in the summer vogue, were not the clothes a girl with money would have chosen. They were off-the-hanger stuff in the misses' department.

"Maybe," suggested Bill, "she's a brain, eh?"

"Pawff," said I.

For the poor girl, as daft with love as her handsome table companion, was putting on a terrific act. She was arch, she was coy, she postured and shrugged with all the airs of a beauty queen in the movies. There used to be a word: coquettish. It has been dead these 30 years. She dug it up.

"Order your lunch," ordered Bill.

But I could not take my eyes off the couple. He leaned forward as if not to miss a syllable of her prattle. Her mouth wriggled like a rabbit's as she chattered.

"That," I said, "is the most ill-matched pair I have ever seen in my life."

At one of her witticisms, Heaven forgive it, he laughed, and turned to glance about at the fellow-lunchers, in pity for us, I suppose, for not having so beautiful a girl as he had. The man was loony. But superbly handsome. His head was splendid, he had broad shoulders, balanced, as no padding could simulate. His features were striking. The hands he moved as he spoke were fine. He was one whale of a good-looking young man, a thoroughbred, a gent, a signor. But the girl...! The waitress came, wide, and cut off my view. So I ordered.

"When you come to think of it," I said to Bill, " nature arranges it as a rule that the good-looking men marry the good-looking girls."

"Not always," corrected Bill. "I've seen some beautiful girls snaffled off by some pretty frowsy-looking males."

"But as a broad general rule," I persisted, "good-looking girls get ·the choice of the best-looking men. It is Nature's way of insuring the improvement of the stock."

"Unless money," pointed out Bill, "or brains interfere with Nature. If a girl has money, she usually has a pretty good choice. And often, if a girl has brains, she can wangle a handsome one."

"Well, obviously, this one over here," I gestured with my butter knife, "has neither money nor brains. And look what she's..."

"They'll hear you," protested Bill.

"My dear man," I soothed him, "they are unaware of anything in this world but each other. Besides, this is clinical. It is my business to query such mysteries as this."

Bill Milne has detested my clinics intensely, ever since we were eight years old.

"There are no mysteries," declared Bill. "There is always an explanation, a rationalization of everything. Maybe the boy is dumber than a coconut."

"Not him," I assured. "A man with that head, that bearing, those hands, shoulders..."

The waitress came and blocked the view again, as she broadly spread our dishes before us. Even the most engrossing clinical interests fade when poached flounder is set before me, with dry toast, hard butter, a large plate of cold cress and one boiled potato green with sprinkled parsley. I bent.

"There," said Bill quietly, "goes your mystery!"

I spun around in my chair.

The young Adonis was up on his feet, moving around to assist his beauteous lady to rise. They were about to leave.

The young Adonis had long, spindly legs, out of all proportion to the rest of him. They dangled out from under his smart tweed sport coat. They ruined his whole appearance. His knees were bent. He looked like a stuffed torso on stilts.

Solicitously, he bent and drew the chair back for his pouting lady.

She rose, flounced out her skirt. She was lithe, willowy, extraordinarily graceful in every line and movement as she flounced down the aisle amidst the tables, all eyes on her.

No wonder the spindle-legged dope was in love with her!

"See?" said Bill. "It is Nature trying to strike a balance."

The Maître D'

JOE CARRE, proprietor of the Six Pines Inn, did us the honor of coming over to our table and greeting us ceremoniously.

"Ah, Mr. Clark!" he exclaimed, loudly enough to make the other diners turn to look. "AND Mr. Herriot!"

He shook hands with us.

The Six Pines Inn, on a beautiful hilltop along the super-highway, is not one of those places you might run in for a hamburger or a hot dog.

It has swank. It has elegance. You should have white-wall tires to drive in on to its rich gravel parking area.

"How is business, Joe?" I inquired.

"Couldn't be better," said Joe.

In his neat black, he looked the perfect Continental maitre d'. In fact, though he owns the place, he calls himself the maitre d'. And that is what is printed on the door of his office as you come in the lobby.

He opened the Six Pines last fall, "to cater," as he said then, "to those people on the highway who want anything BUT a hamburger."

Thus, for around two bucks, you can get a very attractive little meal, though you CAN spend $4 on a steak if you like. The main thing you get at the Six Pines Inn is the feeling of gracious living.

"How's it look?" he asked, low.

It looked perfect. The wide gleaming picture windows, the slim artistic drapes, the well-spaced snowy white tables; the quiet, the soft-moving waitresses, starched; the feeling of inner sunlight.

Joe drew a chair over and sat down.

"There's just one thing missing," he confided softly.

"To give this place the final, supreme touch, I need to know people when they come in, and I should be able, like the true maitre d', to walk up to them, and bow, and call them by name. Like I did you, just now."

"Ah, that'll take time, Joe," I said. "As your business increases, as it is bound to do, you'll get to recognize..."

"Nonsense!" said Herriot. "It's as easy as pie."

"How do you mean?" inquired Joe and I.

"Look," said Herriot. "Every maitre d' in the world is up to tricks to learn the names of important-looking guests. He tips the bellboys in the hotel to slip him the names of imposing people. That business of the maitre d' calling people by name is a sheer racket."

"I don't see..." began Joe.

"You stand," said Herriot, "at that entrance, part of the time, don't you? And you see the cars pulling up on the gravel? And you can spot a real swell car from the ordinary medium-priced cars?"

"Sure," agreed Joe.

"And you can tell," said Herriot, "the minute they get out of the car, whether they are swells or not?"

"Sure."

"Well, all you do," said Herriot, "is note down the license number of the car and walk back into your office. How much is long distance to the city?"

"Twenty cents," said Joe.

"And for 20 cents," said Herriot, "you dial the license bureau at the Parliament Buildings. And you ask the name of the owner of such-and-such a car."

"Holy Moses!" cried Joe.

"By the time," went on Herriot, "they have come into the lobby and checked their hats, you come out of your office, draw yourself up joyously in the pleasure of recognition, call the gentleman by name, and ask him if you may show his party to a table."

"Wow!" said Joe, so excitedly that most of the diners turned to glance at our table again.

"It only works," reminded Herriot, "during the daytime, and on week days when the bureau's open."

"The beauty of it is," I contributed, "think how impressed all the other customers will be to see you greeting distinguished guests by name."

"It's ALL," said Joe, rising, "this place needs."

"Will you try it?" asked Herriot.

"I'll try it now!" said Joe.

From our table, we could see Joe standing at the big entrance window. The next three parties of guests were non-gracious-living types, and Joe smiled at them and left the head waitress to do the conducting.

Then we saw Joe glance at us and wave.

We saw him peering intently out at the parking gravel. He stepped smartly out of sight into his office.

Presently, into the lobby came a party of four—an elderly, imposing-looking man with three elderly ladies, all gracious-living types.

They stood in the lobby gazing about while the man checked his hat.

Then Joe appeared from his office.

"Mr. Calhoun!" he exclaimed, advancing on the gentleman and executing a slight, correct bow.

Mr. Calhoun was surprised and pleased.

"Why, hello?" he said.

"I am Joseph," said Joe, "the maitre d'. It is a pleasure to see you, sir! May I show your party to a table?"

The ladies were even more surprised and pleased than Mr. Calhoun. They glowed at Joe as upon an old friend and retainer.

"Joseph," said the leading lady, obviously Mrs. Calhoun, "let us have a table near a window."

You could see she was taking possession of Joseph, now and for many a party to come.

Joe was magnificent as he led them to a table, smiling with that benign and knowing smile reserved for the maitre d' the world over.

When he got a chance, he came over to us.

"Oh, gosh!" he whispered. "What an idea!"

And he went back to stand at the window of the lobby for more game.

Two or three more non-gracious parties arrived, which Joe let pass.

Then we saw him go on point. He threw us a swift signal and nipped into his office.

In the entrance came a fine handsome young woman in her thirties, followed by a tall sporting gentleman with that all-year-round tan look that the sports-car, winter-in-Bermuda set wear.

Having no hat to check, they came right through the lobby and were shown to a table by one of the waitresses before Joe came out of his office.

Glancing in, he spotted the couple just settling down.

"Ah!" he cried, advancing. "Mr. and Mrs. McTurfy!"

The couple seemed to freeze.

They stared up in horror at Joe.

"How DO you DO?" said Joe, bowing.

The lady struggled to her feet and with averted face walked out of the dining room, the gentleman hastily at her heels. Joe followed, astonished. As they went out the door, they beckoned Joe to follow.

Joe came back in.

"It seems," said Joe, drawing up a chair, "that it was MRS. McTurfy, all right, in the McTurfy car. But the gentleman was NOT Mr. McTurfy."

"Aha!" said Herriot and I.

"He offered me 10 bucks," said Joe.

"Did you take it?" asked Herriot.

"No."

"You'll never make a maitre d'," said Herriot.

The Champion

C HAMPIONS are not always impressive to look at. One of the
greatest I have seen was a meek little bald-headed man with his
spectacles askew, standing in the witness box in a crowded
courtroom.

Maybe you knew that the courts are very concerned these days about
the difficulty of persuading people to appear as witnesses. Most of us
instinctively duck away from the scene of an accident, for instance, lest
we be tangled up in a time-wasting, highly unprofitable and often
humiliating experience. We just don't want to be pushed around by
lawyers and judges (who are ex-lawyers), some of whom forget that the
ordinary citizen is no longer a peasant.

This mild, meek little man in the witness box was the key witness in a
case I was reporting. He had given his answers to the crown attorney
briefly, clearly, and with a curious air of righteousness. It was most
damaging to the accused.

The lawyer for the defense was a famous member of the profession;
and when you get a lawyer who is also a character, watch your step.

He was elderly, handsome, florid. From years of success at his trade,
he had developed a curious drawling, oratorical manner of speech. He
had all the vocal tricks of an actor—a ham Shakespearian actor. He
could roar, boom, wheedle, insinuate. He had a magnificent command
of language.

His normal opening gambit, when handling a dumb little witness like
this one, and a dangerous one, was to phrase his opening questions in
such flowery and ornate terms as to intimidate and confuse the poor soul.
A lawyer can phrase a question that is perfectly understandable by a
judge, but is Greek to the witness. The witness becomes muddled.

Standing forth, his gown flung back, the famous lawyer opened as
expected. Rolling and chewing his words, half chanting, half howling,
he asked a question about 50 words long, all lost in circumlocutions and

parabolics.

The meek, righteous little witness looked stunned.

"Answer me!" thundered the lawyer. The judge and the crowded court all sat back, like box-seat holders for the show.

In two minutes of questions, the lawyer had the poor little man a jelly, stuttering, looking helplessly about. Who would have taken him for a champion?

"Answer the question please," admonished the judge, gently.

"Your Honor," said the meek little man, leaning confidentially toward the judge. "I think this man is drunk."

There was a shocked silence.

"Pptt! Tut-tut!" exploded the startled judge. "You must not say that. Answer the learned counsel's question!"

The old lawyer, so thunderstruck himself that he did look a little fuddled, rolled out another of his characteristic yowling, ham-actor questions, weaving and swaying histrionically.

The bald little champion bent forward and stared intently at the lawyer. Then he turned to the judge.

"Your Honor, I can't make out what he's talking about. He talks queer. I do believe, Your Honor, he has been drink..."

The judge pounded the bench. The court was a panic.

"Does a witness," cried the little champion, shrilly, "have to be talked to by a lawyer who has been..."

The court was hastily adjourned for five minutes, not to ascertain whether the barrister was sober, which, of course, he was, but to let the judge get into his chambers behind the court to have hysterics.

When the case resumed, the famous lawyer, ruffled, subdued, wing-clipped, almost mute, lost the case in no time flat.

The Trap

"PHEW!" said George Wilkie. "Phee-YOO!" A cloud of yellow dust swirled off the gravel road as two cars swept past. We were enveloped.

"We've got to DO something about it!" declared Wilkie hotly.

Four of us were sitting on the flagstone patio at the back of Wilkie's cottage.

Another car from the opposite direction rushed past, and a cloud rolled at us.

"Awfff!" said Henderson, whose cottage was fourth along the road. "Let's take our chairs around in front."

It was glary hot out in front, on the beach side of the cottage. That's why we had picked the shade on the back patio.

"Would you believe," asked Wilkie, as we carried the aluminum chairs around the side, "that seven years ago, that road was just two ruts in the bush?"

"That's a fact," confirmed Henderson. "When Wilkie and I first moved in here, those two ruts were our only access to our cottages. NOW look at it!"

As we set our chairs in the hot sun, we could see the dust floating down on us over the roof every time a car whooshed past.

"Why," asked Cooper, who, like me, was a visitor, "don't you get the township to do something? Put oil, or that salt stuff on the..."

Wilkie and Henderson snorted.

"Township!" said Wilkie. "We've petitioned the township, with over 100 property owners on it. We've written to the provincial Highways Department and they say it's not their problem. We've called in person on every member of the township council..."

"Our food tastes gritty," said Henderson. "The dust goes through the screens. We have to keep all our windows and doors shut. On a summer holiday. Imagine!"

"Yes, sir," said Wilkie, ruefully, "seven years ago there were only 11 cottages on this lake. We had to come in by that side road back a mile, and then follow the ruts through the bush. It was just a farmer's tote road. We thought we had a private access road for years to come..."

"Five years ago, there were 20 cottages," chimed in Henderson. "Then 40. Now there are 100. And the township IMPROVED the road at the urgent request of the cottagers."

Another swirl of dust descended on us.

"Our two ruts," said Wilkie, "are now hooked up with the highways of the continent of North America. Cars from Ohio and New Mexico, Massachusetts and Oregon, and all the provinces of Canada, now whirl along towing trailers full of camp equipment, and boats, looking for some place to camp in the Great Outdoors!"

"Well, look," I said, "surely you know the highway traffic cops. Couldn't you persuade them to come in occasionally and just park here and there to sort of...?"

"Cops!" said Wilkie bitterly. "They go through here at 60!"

Cooper suddenly slapped his leg and stood up.

"Gentlemen," he said. "That reminds me! A friend of mine named Fred Dacy, of London, Ont., had this same problem; and he solved it."

"How?"

"The Dacy System!" exclaimed Cooper. "Look here. Where can we find a couple of wooden boxes? About this big?"

Cooper held his hands to show a box about a foot and a half square.

"There's some wooden boxes under my boathouse," said Wilkie.

We all walked down to the boathouse, and Cooper extracted from under it a couple of wooden boxes of the kind canned goods sometimes come in.

"Perfect!" he said, holding them up. "Now, gentlemen, I trust you both have barbecues?"

Wilkie and Henderson admitted they had.

"The kind that sit on metal legs?" asked Cooper.

They nodded.

"Bring me the legs," he said. "Now, for some black paint, and some yellow plastic clothes line."

"What," we all asked, "goes on?"

"And," said Cooper, "five or six empty tin cans. New ones."

"Look here..." said Wilkie, doubtfully.

"And," said Cooper, "some children's toys. Largish ones, like toy

114

trucks, toy tractors. Red preferred.''

"Aw, now,'' reasoned Henderson.

"Gentlemen,'' said Cooper, "I have to have these things for the Dacy System of Dust Control.''

Wilkie got the black paint from the boathouse—a tin of stove enamel. Henderson walked back up the road to his cottage and returned with the legs off his barbecue, a roll of yellow plastic clothes line, and four or five children's toys, assorted, broken, but mostly red in color.

"These do?'' he asked Cooper.

Cooper was busy slapping stove enamel on the boxes. It dried in quickly.

"Now, gentlemen,'' said he, "we will survey the situation and see what portion of the road you wish Dust Controlled.''

We all went out to the gravel road. Wilkie figured 100 yards west of him would solve the problem. Henderson, whose cottage was 100 yards east, agreed to 100 yards beyond him.

We then carried the black boxes at Cooper's direction, together with barbecue legs, clothes line, children's toys and some empty tin cans from which Cooper tore the labels.

On the south side of the road, on a slightly elevated bank, Cooper set one box on legs. He faced it slightly to the east, with the open side at the back. In the box he set some tin cans and a couple of children's toys arranged, side by side and on top of one another, in a most mysterious and technological fashion.

From the box he ran two strands of yellow clothes line down to the ditch of the road and buried the ends in the earth, securing them with a stone.

We walked the 300 yards, avoiding cars and dust clouds, to the far side of Henderson's, and there, on the north side of the road, we set up the other black box on legs, its open rear scientifically equipped with shiny tin cans and red toys; and with yellow clothes lines down from it to the ditch.

Before we could carry our chairs back to the patio, the magical effect was already evident.

Cars from the east, seeing the mysterious box facing west, would slam on brakes, bob, bow respectfully, and proceed past us at 20, 25, and hardly any dust. Cars from the west, spotting the dark device facing east, its technological innards glowing, would do the same.

For three-quarters of an hour we sat in dustless comfort, serenely accepting the genuflections of the braking cars.

"Heck!" exclaimed Wilkie. "Here comes the police cruiser!"

At 60, in a great cloud, it came; slammed on its brakes, bobbed, backed up; and out got the constable.

We walked down to greet him, as he inspected the contraption on the road bank.

"The children," explained Wilkie. "They're all playing traffic control these days, instead of westerns."

"Aaaah!" said the constable. "No harm, I guess."

"And," said Wilkie, as the constable got back in his car, "educational!"

The Faux Pas

WHEN a man named Curley Christian died recently, several thousand rather special Canadians, on hearing the news, did one or other of the things men do on such occasions: took off their hats, or stood up, or saluted, or closed their eyes a minute and said a prayer, or just smiled. Smiled the particular smile which men reserve to aim at St. Peter himself, there at the Gate.

There are a great many little stories to tell about Curley Christian. But this is the one they like the best.

It was on the latest Royal visit. Curley's friends had got him a reserved seat along the Royal route. When the procession came nigh, the crowds swarmed against the front rows.

Curley stood up.

"Take off your hat!" shouted a woman behind Curley, a patriotic woman, a real Royalist.

Curley turned his radiant smile around on her. She had pushed indignantly forward.

"I would be obliged," laughed Curley, "if you would take it off for me."

The poor creature was now near enough, in her fervid indignation, to see the artificial arms hanging beside Curley. And when her gaze, agonized enough, went farther, she could see Curley's artificial legs.

I regret to say she did not remove Curley's hat for him, while the Princess passed. It is doubtful if she saw the Princess, even; for she slunk away, and may be slinking still, for all I know. Curley Christian had lost both legs at the knee and both arms at the elbow in the Vimy Battle long, long ago, and lived 37 years a happy man, going to the races, playing gin rummy, attending meetings, speaking and standing forth for his comrades, an inspiration to all those with lesser fates who might grieve for themselves. Curley never grieved. There was enough of him left to be a man among men.

life.''

That poor woman! When I heard Curley was dead, she was the first one I thought of. Can anything be more devastating than a faux pas committed against the helpless? A young woman I know was stricken with polio when she already had one small child and was expecting another. Paralyzed from the waist down, she none the less brought forth a perfect son. With great patience she learned to walk again with iron braces on her legs and crutches when she needs them for the fancier efforts. She now runs her home without help, raising her children joyously. She sails a dinghy. Fishes. Drives the car, with certain special attachments.

The other day she had her five-year-old and her two-year-old out for a drive, and they wanted ice-cream cones. Selecting a wayside restaurant, she parked and sent the little five-year-old girl in for three cones.

When the waitress had prepared the cones and taken the money, the little girl said:

''Mummy asks if you would carry them out to the car for me.''

There were doors and steps to negotiate.

''Why doesn't your mummy come in herself?'' growled the girl.

''Well, because...'' replied the five-year-old.

The waitress carried the cones out; and when she saw the fine-looking young woman sitting smiling at the wheel, the injustice of this world suddenly struck her.

Putting on the airs of a lady's maid, she flounced down the steps, ice-cream cones held high, and in an affected voice, presented them, saying:

''Here you are, me lady!''

The car door swung open, to let the little five-year-old in. There, just beyond the proffered cones, were the legs in their braces...
Wow!

This last one I witnessed. It was in the supermarket. A young woman, shy-looking, maybe a little defeated, was pushing a go-cart in which sat a boy of at least four or five.

Two women ahead of me in the cashier lineup nudged one another and stared. I glanced back to see the go-cart coming in back of me.

''For Pete's sake!'' said one of the women, in that slightly cracked husky voice you hear, in supermarkets as often as anywhere. ''Look at that big, overgrown kid being pushed around in a go-cart!''

I glanced at the child, the mother. She must have heard. I glanced at the women. But what compelled my eyes was the lean young man hustling the parcels into bags at the cash register before us.

His face went livid. His dark eyes blazed. He turned white as a ghost.

"Lady," he said, low, through teeth, "that little boy has never walked. Maybe never will."

The two women fumbled up their big paper bags and hurried out of the store wordless. I was next, paid my tab, picked up my bag. The young man never looked at me, but tears were trickling beside his nose. I halted, rearranging my parcels.

"Hello, there," cried the young man.

"Hello," said the young woman.

"Hi, there, Johnnie! How are you today?"

"Fine," sang out the boy.

Curley Christian, wherever you are, answer us this: which is worse? To be unable to lift your hat when a Princess passes by? Or to be a woman who shouts:

"Take off your hat!"

The Wrong Bus

ARDON ME, said the lady in the seat next ahead of me in the bus, "but would you please not smoke your pipe? I am allergic to tobacco smoke."

"Well... uh..." I said. "Certainly ma'am."

With my tough old thumb I stopped the fire.

She had well-groomed white hair, was smartly dressed, and, oh, about 60. The masterful type.

The bus had only been en route 10 minutes, but I already experienced some uneasy feelings. For one thing, it was a much larger bus than the city and suburban buses I am familiar with. Besides, unlike the buses I had just passed in the bus terminal, it was not crowded.

And to lend a slight jolt—right back of me, at the rear of the bus, where I had gone in expectation of a smoke, there was a very small cubicle distinctly marked "Toilet."

Watching out the window, with my extinguished pipe in hand, I observed, in less than 10 minutes, that we were headed north out of the city, not west.

I got up and walked to the front.

"Is this the bus for Guelph?" I asked the driver.

"No, sir. It's the express to North Bay."

"Do we stop anywhere en route?"

"Nope," said the driver, for you are not supposed to disturb bus drivers.

As I walked back, the lady in the next to last seat held up her finger commandingly.

"You were enquiring about smoking?" she asked.

"No, ma'am," I replied." I have just found out I am on the wrong bus."

After a couple of minutes, she got up and came to sit down beside me.

"You poor man," she said. "How did you happen to get on the wrong bus?''

"If I knew that," I explained, "I wouldn't be here. To save me the trouble and confusion of the bus terminal, a friend got me my ticket for Guelph yesterday. At the terminal, I found a person in uniform to whom I showed my ticket. And it directed me to the lineup of this bus."

"It?" said the lady.

"Yes," I said. "It had long hair down to its shoulders and a round face. You couldn't tell whether it was a he or a she. So it's an it, isn't it?''

She gave me that sideways stare that is far more menacing than the fullface stare ladies possess. She studied me while I looked out the window at the passing suburbs.

"What business are you in?" she asked firmly.

"No business, ma'am," I replied.

"Retired?"

"No, to tell the truth, lady," I said, "I am just a storyteller."

Another long study period.

"Can you tell me a story?" she asked, for she was obviously the type of lady who desires conversation.

I then had my fiendish inspiration.

"Can I tell you a shaggy dog story?" I said.

"Is it clean?" she asked, sharply.

"Ma'am!" I said, shocked, for I have a venerable appearance.

"Go ahead," she suggested, relaxing.

"Now, this story," I began, "was told me by my grandson, who is a press photographer. And they get the best stories. It seems there was a man who lived in a fine frame house for years. A good, comfortable frame house. But he came up in the world, and he decided that rather than move to a better house, he would simply brick over his frame house."

"Excellent insulation," agreed the lady.

"He knew some bricklayers, and also the manager of a brickyard. They all came on the weekend and carefully measured the house. They then figured out just exactly how many bricks they would need for the job. Well, they finished bricking over the house. But they had one brick left over."

"Yes?" said my seat mate.

"One brick. Now, the point of the story is: what did they do with that surplus brick?''

"Throw it at Trudeau? Use it for a doorstopper?" guessed the lady.

"No. Now, the point is: what did they do with that surplus brick? THINK about it. Just keep THINKING about that spare brick!"

She stared at me.

"Go ahead," she said.

"No. That's all there is," said I.

A more indignant lady I have seldom seen.

"Well, of all the stupid stories I ever heard..." she stated.

She gazed about the bus, prospecting for somebody else to talk to. But there were none that looked available. So she decided to sit and talk to me.

She told me why she was going to North Bay. She was going to spend a couple of weeks with her daughter. Then next month, she was going to fly out to Vancouver to spend a month with her other daughter. It seems both her daughters had married men not quite up to what she had expected.

As the miles reeled past, and we left the last suburbs, which are pretty far distant from the city these days, she had got onto her own marriage—which was not quite what she had expected, either.

But when you are on the wrong bus, what can you do? I thought of feigning sleep. However, we were getting into the handsome country north of the city, and I was able to view it even while the lady went on and on.

After about an hour and a half, and a good 100 and some miles on our way to North Bay, I caught her running out of wind.

"Could I tell you another story?" I interrupted.

"Is it as stupid as the last one?" she asked crisply.

"Stupider," I assured her. The bowl of my pipe still in my hand was cold as a trout. "But you reminded me of it. It seems there was this gentleman sitting at the back of a bus and he took out a cigar and started to light it."

" 'Pardon me,' said the lady across the aisle from him. 'But I am allergic to cigar smoke. Would you please not smoke?' "

"Now, this lady had a small French poodle on her lap. The man said: 'Right. But I'll make you a deal. I am allergic to poodles. You get rid of your poodle, and I'll get rid of my cigar.' "

"The bus was within three miles of its destination. The lady opened the bus window and dropped the poodle out. The gentleman gallantly opened his window, and threw his cigar out."

My seat mate was listening with that sideways stare.

123

"When they reached their destination, the lady said to the gentleman, 'Wait a couple of minutes.' And they waited. And suddenly appeared the little poodle, galloping joyously. And what do you think it was carrying in its mouth?"

"The cigar!" cried my seat mate delightedly.

"No," said I. "The brick."

"The what?" she demanded.

"The brick!" said I. "That surplus brick that was left over from that frame house they..."

She drew back on the bus seat. She took a deep breath. She stared, speechless; picked up her purse; got up, went to her seat ahead of mine, reached up and got a small travelling case from the rack; moved up 10 seats forward to an empty place. I lit my pipe.

And when we arrived in North Bay, she didn't even give me a backward glance as we filed off.

I am having a happy visit in North Bay, have phoned several old friends to visit me, have written a letter of thanks to my grandson, the press photographer, and this story to explain to my friend in Guelph how I caught the wrong bus.

The Push

T HE car wouldn't start.

It being one of these slick modern jobs, all you do is turn the ignition key, and the starter obediently goes row-row-row-row, and then the engine leaps to life.

But in my cluttered garage (ladders, lawn hoses, garden chairs, etc., stored for the winter) all it did was go row-row-row, and nothing leaped at all.

A strong odor of gasoline became evident.

Now, I am not in the habit of having engine trouble. Engines baffle me. They frighten me. All my life, I have treated them with the same distant respect I have afforded hornets' nests. I placate them. I pamper them, pander to them. If it says on the sticker on the instrument panel "Oil should be changed every 1,000 miles," I have it changed every 850 miles. If the dealer who sold me the car mails me a folder advising a check-up and overhaul before winter sets in, I take the car in next day and have it overhauled and checked up. Same in spring. Same in autumn. I am not in the habit of having engine trouble. At the slightest cough, sneeze, squeak or tick from my engine, I rush it in terror to the nearest service station.

In consideration of all this respect and tender care, you can understand my indignation as I twisted the key, and all the dang thing did was go row-row-row, without the slightest sign of any intention of responding.

"Don't run the battery down," said my wife from the garage door. (It's her job to close it, after I back out.)

"I smell gas!" I reported sharply.

Sure enough, the air was thick with fumes.

"It's flooding!" I announced.

"What does that mean?" inquired my wife.

As we have owned automobiles for 38 years, that will indicate how little engine trouble we have had.

"Well," I replied, "it means something's stuck, I guess."

"What do we do?" asked my wife.

We went in the house and took off our coats, abandoning our plan to go shopping.

I telephoned the dealer from whom we bought the car and informed him of this outrageous situation. The service manager said his emergency truck was booked up for three hours at least.

"Are you a member of the A.A.A.?" he asked.

"Yes."

"Call them," said he. "They'll fix it in a minute. It sounds to me as if it's just flooded."

I called the A.A.A., and the girl said she would have somebody right over.

"We shouldn't get so upset," said my wife, "over a little delay like this."

"I'm not upset," I declared.

"After all, we were just going shopping," she reasoned. "Nothing important."

"I'm not upset," I repeated distinctly. "I just think that an engine that gets as much care and respect as ours has no right..."

"Don't work yourself up," advised my wife.

"I don't abuse it," I insisted. "I don't drive at excessive speeds like everybody else; I don't leave it out in the cold; I give it the very best oil, the top grade gas..."

"Look!" said my wife. "It isn't a person. It's a car."

"Instead of every 1,000 miles," I reminded her, "I change oil every..."

There was a ring at the doorbell, and it was the service truck sent by the A.A.A.; a cheery, husky young man in dirty brown overalls and no hat.

We went to the garage. He got in the car and tried the key. The starter growled lustily.

"Smell the gas?" I called to him.

He bailed out and lifted the hood.

"She's flooded, all right," said he, after tinkering. "I'll have to give you a push. You get in and steer it back."

To my astonishment, the husky young man crouched down and shoved the car back out of the garage to the street, where his truck waited.

He came around and spoke to me in the window.

"Do you know how to handle a push in these automatic drives?"

"No," I confessed.

"Put the handle down to low," he said. "Low. That's right. Now, turn on the ignition key. O.K. Now, when I start pushing you, put your foot down on the gas, right to the floor."

"Right down?"

"Yes. Push her down right to the floor."

"O.K."

The street on which I live is called Crescent Road. It really isn't a crescent at all, but a serpent. It twists and turns. It has all the vagrant meanderings of a cow path. I live on one of the meanders.

The truck eased up behind me. I felt it take a bold grip on my rear.

I gripped the wheel, glanced at "LOW," saw the ignition key was turned, and I reached out firmly with my right foot and tramped the pedal DOWN.

I faced the street, holding steady and cool.

Traffic was coming toward me—two cars, a bus and a panel truck.

Our speed increased.

I steered carefully on my side, and let the two cars, the bus and the panel truck pass. Our speed increased!

Ahead, a car was parked on my side. And, in the distance, around the next bend, a car appearing. Our speed increased!

Would I make it around the parked car before the oncoming car reached it? Could the driver of my truck see the dilemma approaching?

Good heavens! He was still increasing speed! He was going to try to make it!

Make it? Our speed was mounting furiously. We must be going fifty. SIXTY!

The oncoming car braked, and I swooped around the parked car.

SIXTY! Why, the infernal fool must be shoving me at SEVENTY!

Ahead, all in a wild blur, was the next curve in Crescent Road, around which anything might be coming.

Gripping the wheel in utter terror, I glared in the rear-view mirror. How could I signal the lunatic to slow down?

There was no truck pushing me. Away back, half a block back, the yellow emergency truck was following.

I nipped my foot up off the floor boards, pedal and gas, all in one paralyzed yank.

I braked, steered to the curb.

The emergency truck overtook me, and the husky young man dropped out and came to my window.

"I thought," I said thickly, "you were pushing me."

"I thought," said he, "you had gone completely nuts!"

I suppose it is best to have a little engine trouble now and again, to sort of acquaint you with things.

The Rescue

"GET OVER HERE," came the strangly voice of old Dandy Daniels on the telephone, "as fast as you know how!"

"Aw, Dandy," I protested. "I'm still in my pyjamas."

"You got to make it fast!" shouted Dandy.

"Look, Dandy..."

"Do you know what this old fool Hortense has done?" rasped Dandy. "She's thrown my slippers out in the garbage!"

"Well, but..."

"The garbage truck hasn't been gone 20 minutes!" yelled Dandy. "Get over here fast, and we'll catch 'em. Fast!"

He hung up violently.

What can you do with an irate old man like Dandy Daniels! I suppose there is one like him in every family connection. Away over 80, he lives in tidy comfort with Hortense, who has been his housekeeper for over 40 years. Poor soul.

It was Hortense I had in mind as I hastily threw on my clothes in preparation to drive over to Dandy's. How in the world had she thrown Dandy's slippers out in the garbage?

It was only three weeks ago that I had driven Dandy downtown to buy the slippers. He had seen them advertised in one of those after-Christmas sales: regular $5.95 for only $3.95.

Dandy's only remaining hobby now is saving, collecting, gouging, amassing, gypping and otherwise acquiring money. And at his urgent command, I had taken him down to save $2 on a nice new pair of house slippers.

Yes, it was for Hortense I hustled off to Dandy's.

He was waiting on his front steps when I drew up.

"You take your time, don't you!" he yelped, as he tottered down the walk. "That garbage truck will be miles from here by now."

"Now, think, Dandy," I suggested, as he groaned into the car. "How do we know where the truck has gone?"

"Step on it!" commanded Dandy. "You don't think I've lived all these years in this neighborhood without knowing what route the garbage trucks follow? They go six blocks straight up. And then turn left one block, and down the next six blocks."

"Why, Dandy, darlin'," I pointed out, "your slippers will be buried under tons of garbage."

"You drive," said Dandy. "I'll do the thinking."

"How," I asked kindly, "did poor Hortense come to throw the slippers out?"

"Poor Hortense my knuckle!" cried Dandy. "She did it deliberately!"

Well, of course, this was preposterous. Hortense? Why, Hortense had intended, as a young woman, to be a missionary in Darkest Africa. She became Dandy's housekeeper instead. Which is much the same thing.

"Deliberately?" I scoffed.

"Sure," said Dandy. "She's been at me ever since I got the new ones to throw them out. And this morning..."

"You mean," I gasped, incredulous, "it's your OLD slippers she threw out?"

You never saw such things. Dandy must have had them 30 years. Shapeless, ghastly old fleece-lined slippers, not only flattened at the heel, but gone away over to the sides. A filthy grey color, they flap-flapped with every step.

I braked the car.

"We're not chasing THOSE old monstrosities!" I declared.

"You keep going!" gritted Dandy, turning the turkey-red color that betokens trouble for all. "You don't figure I'm wearing those new slippers EVERY day, do you? Come on! Step on it!"

"Dandy," I finally said. "You ought to be ashamed of yourself. With all your money..."

"Oho!" cut in Dandy. "And how do you think I got my money? By throwing out things that have years of useful..."

We overtook the garbage truck on the short block where it had turned left.

It was heaped high. Some of the cargo was packed in neat paper bags, in compliance with the civic by-law; most of it was done up in loose and dampish wrappings of newspaper; but much of it was just loose—tin cans, sloppy cartons, peelings, parings, bones.

130

The brown-overalled crew of three was busy heaving more on to the pyramid.

We pulled up behind the truck.

"Hi, boys!" said Dandy affably, bailing out.

"Why, hello Mr. Daniels," said the boys apprehensively.

"I got a pair of slippers," said Dandy, "got into your load by accident back at my place. I wonder could you help me locate them?"

The crew glanced at one another.

"Why, Mr. Daniels," said the boldest and biggest, "I'm afraid they'd be pretty deep in there now. Four or five feet down."

"It won't take a minute," said Dandy, making as if to climb up the side of the truck. "Just you boys lend me a hand. We'll poke through..."

"We couldn't do that, Mr. Daniels! It's against the regulations. The inspector might be along any minute."

"Here," said Dandy to me. "Give me a boost."

"Now, now, Dandy!" I said.

But up he went, with four of us boosting. And two of the boys climbed on to show how hopeless it was.

With a broken hockey stick he found on the load, Dandy strenuously dug and flung, the boys catching, so that the parcels and cans did not fall off on to the pavement.

"Aha!" cried Dandy, stooping and picking up a decayed pair of spectacles. "See what people lose?"

He wiped the decrepit glasses on a piece of newspaper and pocketed them.

A minute later, he stooped again and came up with a tin.

"See?" he cried. "A full tin of spaghetti sauce! Some reckless housewife, wasting her husband's earnings."

"Somebody," said one of the boys, "bought two tins for 29 cents, and didn't like the first one."

Before he was winded, Dandy unearthed a perfectly good tin pie plate, a spoon a little the worse for wear, and a ragged grey cardigan to which various items of cargo adhered.

"You boys," he said, "don't realize what valuable property you are carting away."

"I tell you what," said the largest and boldest of the sanitation staff. "When we dump the truck at the incinerator, Mr. Daniels, we'll keep our eyes skinned for your slippers, eh? Won't we, boys?"

131

He gave me a wink.

The others agreed heartily.

I drove Dandy, muttering, home.

At 8 p.m., he telephoned me in high excitement.

"Hey!" he cried. "One of the boys brought me my slippers!"

"No!"

"They got 'em!" crowed Dandy. "That big fella brought them just a minute ago."

"I hope you rewarded him properly."

"Certainly I did!" snorted Dandy. "I tipped him a quarter."

Loud Speaker

L EW BURGESS, who has the fifth cottage up the beach from ours, is one of those soft-speaking men, and I am having a little difficulty hearing him now, as my ears are really starting to fail. All dressed up in collar and tie, and wearing his blue blazer with the Air Force crest on it, Lew turned his outboard into my dock, where I was sitting thinking.

He is in real estate.

"Mumble, mumble, beedle deedle," he said, holding on to my dock. "Squeedle feedle Semple."

"You'll have to speak up, Lew," I apologized.

"I was saying," yelled Lew, "I've just been down at The Lodge seeing that old Mr. Semple."

"Oho?" I said. "Business, eh?"

"Waw," said he. "Squaddle feep doohoo, cammy thun forpass thumbunny."

"Thumbunny, eh?" I said, with interest. "Speak up!"

"Barfle," he said, "whee Semple bungit fab, Semple daggit woof."

Now, I am really interested in Mr. Semple. He is a rich old industrialist who has been coming up to The Lodge, the only summer hotel on our lake, for the past 30 years. He is, in fact, the most distinguished citizen in our entire summer colony.

So I reached out and pulled Burgess's outboard skiff closer along the dock to bring him right beside me.

"Start over again, Lew," I said. "And speak up."

It is hard for Lew to speak up. He is a natural-born soft speaker.

But he did his best. And as I listened to his story, I could not help smiling at the sight of him, and the way his mouth contorted with the effort of speaking loud.

It seems Burgess's firm had discovered that old Mr. Semple's corporation was in the market to buy four or five acres of suburban land for a warehouse. And they had telephoned Burgess to call on him and describe a perfectly marvellous site they had, 500 yards from a clover leaf off a main throughway.

"I gave him the particulars," shouted Lew, "and he was mighty interested. But he said that Burkfielder, of Burkfielder, Flint and Mutch, our biggest competitors in industrial real estate, was coming up this afternoon to see him about another site."

"Not QUITE so loud, Lew," I said. "You remind me of the people my Uncle Ed Cantelon used to play his joke on. He used to introduce people after telling them, privately, that the other was deaf. So he'd have them yelling at each other, louder and louder, until they both got mad."

Lew Burgess was staring at me with a wild surmise. He reached up and grabbed my arm to interrupt me.

"It means a lot to me," he yelled, "if I can pin down this Semple deal. I'm due for a partnership in our firm any time."

"Good," said I, waving my hand to soften him down.

"Burkfielder," he shouted, "has to come to The Landing in his car and get a taxi launch to bring him to The Lodge."

It's four miles.

"Tell me again about your Uncle Ed," he bellowed.

So I told him what a practical joker Uncle Ed Cantelon had been, in his quiet way.

"Come on?" cried Lew. "Get in. For the heck of it! I owe it to you."

Lew drove his outboard back down to The Lodge two miles east.

We walked from their fancy wharf across the neat lawns. Mr. Semple, whom I know by sight, was sitting on the veranda surrounded by a bevy of rapt ladies and gentlemen in shorts, listening to his discourse on the state of the nation.

"Hello, Burgess, back again?" he called.

"It just occurred to me," said Burgess, apologizing with gestures to the other guests, "that I might pick up Mr. Burkfielder at The Landing and bring him over to see you. It will save time for both of you, and I have nothing better to do."

"Very decent of you," said Mr. Semple. "Nice way to treat a rival in business. Good idea."

"What time," asked Lew, "is he expected?"

"I told him to get here around 4," said Mr. Semple, "after I've had my nap."

"Very good, sir," said Lew. "And by the way, I thought I should mention that Mr. Burkfielder is a little hard of hearing. You have to speak clearly..."

"Ah, thanks," said Mr. Semple. "Nothing worse than trying to make a deal with a man who can't hear. All kinds of misunderstandings."

As we walked back to the skiff across the foolish lawns and sunburned flower beds with which summer hotels try to convert the beautiful wilds into mere suburbs, I looked at Burgess with fresh interest. He had always appeared to me to be such a soft-spoken, innocent sort of guy.

"We'll pick Burkfielder up," said Lew, "and...uh..."

"Better get to The Landing," I suggested, "well before 4."

We got there, in fact, well before 3.

Around 3:30, a big red-and-white convertible drove on to the wharf at The Landing where we were waiting, and Lew said:

"Hi, Mr. Burkfielder!"

"Hello, Burgess," said Burkfielder, surprised. "What are you doing here?"

"I live here," said Lew. "My cottage is just across the lake. And when Mr. Semple told me you were coming up to see him, I offered to ferry you across."

"Well, that's mighty nice," said Burkfielder, looking anxious.

We showed him where to park his convertible back off the wharf, and as we walked down to Lew's boat, Burkfielder started to explore cautiously.

"So you're a friend of Semple's, eh?"

"Oh, yes," said Lew, "he's been coming up to The Lodge for years. Grand old boy. Do you know him?"

"No, just to see him," said Burkfielder.

"When he mentioned you were coming up," said Lew, "and I said I knew you, he asked me to pick you up to save time. And by the way, you know he's quite hard of hearing, don't you?"

"Ah, thanks," said Burkfielder, as we got into the skiff.

"He doesn't wear a hearing aid," said Lew. "You know how some of these old boys are when they start to..."

(I took no offence.)

"Thanks for the tip," repeated Burkfielder, sinking into the bow seat with his briefcase on his lap.

When we reached The Lodge, Lew escorted Burkfielder on to the veranda, busy with tea. I sat on the steps. Summer hotels don't make my kind of tea.

"Hello, there," greeted Mr. Semple loudly. "Thanks, Burgess. Come into my room, Mr. Burkfielder, just here at the end of the veranda."

Lew came and sat on the steps with me.

Even with the chatter and hum of the guests at tea on the veranda, even with Mr. Semple's door shut, even I could hear the rising sound of voices.

They were loud to begin with.

They got louder.

In a few minutes, Mr. Semple's door opened and out came the two, looking flushed.

Mr. Burkfielder was stuffing things back in his briefcase.

"Well, good day, sir," shouted Mr. Burkfielder.

"Good day to you sir," barked Mr. Semple.

"I'll run you back to The Landing," said Lew, standing up as Burkfielder reached the steps.

"Thanks," said Burkfielder, "I've got to get on back to town."

As we lowered ourselves into Lew's skiff, Burkfielder took a long look back at The Lodge.

"What a cranky old man," he said.

The Switch

I T WAS 11:30 p.m. and my wife and I were putting the last touches on the Christmas tree. (Nothing takes more last touches than a Christmas tree.)

A knock at the front door.

"Who can that be?" said my wife, heading for the pantry door, for she had got into her nightie and house coat an hour ago.

"Some revellers, maybe," I hoped.

I opened the door. And there stood young Henderson, from across the street.

"Hel-LO!" I cried, like Santa Claus.

"Gosh, Mr. Clark," said young Henderson, nipping in the door, "I'm sorry to..."

"Come on in," I said. "In half an hour I can wish you a merry Christmas, lad."

"I'm in an awful spot, Mr. Clark," said Henderson. "And I was just wondering if you or Mrs. Clark could help me out."

"Why sure, boy," I said leading him in so that he could get a view of our Christmas tree all blazing with colored balls and nothing else. No tinsel. No fancy bits. Just a mass of round glowing balls.

I could see, when I looked at him, that young Henderson was in no mood even to notice our tree. He was haggard.

"Nothing the matter, is there?" I inquired hastily.

"There sure is," said Henderson.

Whereupon my wife, listening from the pantry door, came in.

"Oh, Mrs. Clark, I hope I'm not intruding," cried Henderson.

"We're all alone," reassured my wife. "The grandchildren and everybody arrive at crack of day."

"I'm in what is called a... an awful spot!" said Henderson. "And I didn't know what to do until I thought maybe you could help me out. All the stores are closed. I just rushed downtown. But everything is closed..."

"What's the problem?" I asked, authoritatively.

"Could you, would you, by any chance," said Henderson, sinking into a chair and not even noticing our beautiful tree, "have ANYTHING you could spare me, sell me, in the way of a special sort of gift for my wife?"

We looked at young Henderson in some astonishment.

He lives in the lower duplex across the street with his most attractive little wife of three years, and their year-old baby, a beauty.

"You mean," I croaked, "you forgot to get your wife a CHRIST-MAS present!"

"No, no!" said Henderson, "it isn't that. But my wife and I agreed, weeks and weeks ago, that we wouldn't go and spend a lot of money on each other. We solemnly agreed to give each other just some token gift. We've got so many other things to think of. So we solemnly agreed, SOLEMNLY, to just get some little thing, something around $10."

My wife and I looked guiltily at each other.

"Well," said young Henderson, tragically, "I happened to look under the ironing board, not one hour ago. And there it was."

"What?"

"She knows," said Henderson, angrily, "that I've wanted a 12-gauge pump gun ever since we were married. But a 12-gauge pump costs $130 or $140!"

"She got you the gun?"

"She PROMISED," said Henderson, "not to spend more than $10 on each other. And there it is. I saw the box. It's the gun!"

"And what have you got her?" I asked.

"Twelve," said young Henderson hollowly, "fifty! A pair of those great big hairy mule bedroom slippers the girls are wearing!"

"Oh, my poor boy!" said my wife.

We sat silent, shocked at his plight.

"I'm sorry to come in like this," said young Henderson, "but it just occurred to me, in my desperation, that you, being sort of older people, might have some Christmas gift, something more expensive, something that you might perhaps be willing to SELL me."

"Darling," I said to my wife, "this is a situation that calls for some thought. How about you getting us all a cup of tea, at this late hour, with no milk or sugar...?"

My wife got up and headed for the kitchen.

When the swing door shut, I hissed.

"Listen, lad! My wife and I went through the same hocus-pocus. We agreed not to spend any money on each other. Just a token gift. Something around $10 each, and let's put our money on the children..."

Young Henderson was looking at me with radiant hope.

"So I got her," I whispered hastily, "one of those gorgeous alligator purses. Sheer lunacy! Sixty-eight dollars!"

"Oh, marvellous, marvellous!" breathed Henderson.

"But just this evening," I said, "I happened to look behind the bookcase, and I see this box that obviously contains a shirt."

"So?" urged Henderson.

"Rather than embarrass my wife," I said, "by breaking our solemn agreement and giving her this purse, I've been worrying about it all night! Your problem seems to be the answer to my problem!"

"Quick!" hissed Henderson.

I got up and reached in behind the dictionaries in the bookcase and brought out the beautiful gift-wrapped box containing the alligator purse, a crazy extravagance if ever there was one.

"It's gold-mounted," I whispered.

"I'll bring the money over in the morning," Henderson whispered back.

And he dashed out the door.

When my wife came in with the tea, he was gone.

"He thought," I explained, "of something else."

So my wife drank one cup of tea without milk and sugar and I drank the two.

And after a few more pats and twiddles at the Christmas tree, in fond speculation of how our grandchildren would look when they saw it, come break of day and they arrived full of *bonhomie* and birdseed, we set off for bed.

I let my wife precede me, on the pretext of turning off the lights.

She had not got the box with my shirt in it from behind the bookcase to lay with the other gifts at the foot of the tree. I went and got it.

As I lifted it, a curious odor struck my nose.

An odor that filled me with consternation.

I sniffed the box. My heart stood still.

This was no shirt!

This was the buckskin jacket I have wanted for the past 25 years! There is no mistaking the smoky odor of the Indian tanned buckskin.

Sixty dollars it must have cost. Oh, faithless woman! I dropped the box at the foot of the tree. Stealthily, I went out the front door into the freezy night. Across the street I streaked. The Hendersons' flat was all in darkness.

I rang the bell. Rang it, rang it.

Young Henderson's head appeared.

"I'm dreadfully," I gasped, "DREADFULLY sorry, my boy. But I've GOT to have that alligator purse..."

"Ssshhhhh!" said Henderson, whipping out into the hall and closing the door.

"I've GOT to..." I yammered.

"Thank heavens you came," said young Henderson. "Just before we went to bed, I had another look at that long cardboard box. It was too LIGHT for the gun. I peeked. It's a set of those barbecue things—long-handled fork, long-handled spoon. It would be AWFUL if I gave her the purse!"

"Quick!" I hissed.

He tip-toed in and handed me out the lovely gift-wrapped box.

It's at the foot of the tree.

All's well.

But never trust a woman to keep a vow of poverty.

The
Laughing Lady

YOU NEVER know your luck.

For example, I have the weirdest luck at railway ticket-office windows. If there are three wickets, let us say there are four people lined up at two of them and five at the other.

Realizing my bad luck, I move over to one side so that I can appraise the three line-ups in order to figure which one to join. I know perfectly well that if I join any one of the three, the person behind whom I choose to stand, on arriving at his or her turn, will pull a folder out of his pocket or her purse and proceed to buy a round-trip ticket, seven feet long, to Honolulu, with stopovers at numerous scenic cities en route, the features of which he or she will need to inquire into, at length, from the ticket seller.

It always works that way. All I want is a $2 ticket to Hamilton.

Do you think I can pick the right line? At the moment I see the seven-foot ticket hauled out of the drawer by the ticket agent, the other two lines, either of which I could have joined, have just dissolved, and new ones, six people long, have just formed.

It is the same at banks. I want to deposit $8. There are three receiving tellers' wickets open. There are four people in two of the lines and two in the third. I join the one with two. The lady behind whom I fall in is a quiet, middle-aged lady carrying a black silk shopping bag. I figure she is going to cash a quick cheque for $2.

She is cashier for the supermarket up the street; and when she reaches the wicket, she empties out the black silk shopping bag, five piles of currency, three fat packets of cheques and two passbooks to be made up. Meanwhile, the other two lines now have five people in them, all looking like merchants with today's cash to be checked in.

But still, you never know your luck.

I keep my account in an uptown branch near where I live. But sometimes I go into the downtown head-office branch of my bank, where they know me, to cash a cheque in an emergency.

They have often as many as seven or eight tellers working at the long walnut counter. No wickets.

As I came in, taking my cheque from the wallet, I paused to see which of the tellers, all girls, would remember me and not delay to make identifications.

As I stood, two ladies paused beside me. They were medium ladies, maybe 38, maybe 42. Smart, attractive, bright-looking types such as live in those suburbs where the bungalows have double garages.

"Let's get in different lines," said the one in the gray suit, she having taken off a snow-wet tweed topcoat and hung it over her arm. "It'll save time."

"Right," said her companion, in a camel-hair coat.

The two promptly fell in, at the tail end of adjoining lines.

I glanced ahead to pick out a teller I knew. The one I wanted was in the line the lady in the gray suit had just joined.

But as I was about to fall in behind her, a fat, sour-looking gentleman stepped in ahead of me. Indeed, I bumped him slightly, not seeing him taking his place.

"Sorry," I mumbled.

"There's plenty of other lines," he said, very sniffy, giving me a bilious look over his shoulder.

The lines slowly advanced as the customers ahead were dealt with. The two ladies conversed brightly. They both reached the counter together, side by side. The one in the gray suit was the rounded, svelte type who almost invariably drapes herself on a counter, allowing herself to project rather conspicuously to the rear.

She was so draped, while her teller attended her wants, when somebody dropped an umbrella a few yards up the parquet floor to our left, and all heads turned to the left.

The lady in gray, still draped, turned her head. So did the fat, bilious gentleman immediately ahead of me. So did nearly everybody in the several lines. But I was trying to catch the eye of the teller in our line; and so it was that my head was not turned when the other woman, who was on the right of her friend at the counter, quickly reached over and sharply pinched the bottom of her friend, the lady in the gray suit.

The lady in the gray suit sprang upright from draping on the counter, swung around and gave the bilious fat man a resounding slap on the face.

The fat man fell back on me. There was consternation.

With bright, blazing mischievous eyes, the woman in the camel coat was smothering her mirth while trying to calm her friend in gray. The bilious man, speechless, had hurriedly walked off and vanished.

I aimed a narrow accusing eye at the lady in camel.

"Darling!" she hooted to her friend. "It was me!"

The two of them fell forward on the counter and shook.

All I did was reflect that, but for the grace of Heaven and a fat man, I would have been next in line behind the lady in gray.

You never know your luck.

Demonstration

H EY; 'came the voice of my elderly and bossy friend, Mr. Dandy
Daniels, on the phone. "Can you be here at 2 o'clock?"
"Two, Dandy?" I parried. "I'm awfully sorry but..."
"Don't give me any of that stuff," rasped Dandy. "You can make it.
You better get here about 1:30."

"Dandy, look," I explained, "I haven't driven my car for three days
now, on account of a sprained wrist. I slipped on the ice."

"Sprained wrist!" cried old Dandy. "All the better!"

"I beg your pardon?" I protested indignantly.

"You know that roll-top desk in the upstairs hall?" ignored Dandy.

I know it well. It is just one of the pieces of furniture that congest
Dandy's small, tidy and old-fashioned house in a rather run-down
neighborhood of the city. Dandy has been living there for over 40 years
with his aged housekeeper, Hortense, and due to a certain tight-
fistedness in the character of old Dandy, the house has slowly accumu-
lated more bric-a-brac and furnishings than it can conveniently accom-
modate.

"I've decided," said Dandy, "to move the desk down to the ground
floor. It will be handier."

"Well, for Pete's sake," I exclaimed. "You're not suggesting that I
help you move that thing down..."

"Keep your shirt on!" yelped Dandy. "I'm not asking you to lay a
hand on it. All I want is you to be HERE, at 1:30."

"Please, Dandy," I reasoned, "use your head. That old desk must
weigh 300 pounds. You've got to get some regular furniture movers in to
help bring it down those narrow stairs of yours."

"Furniture movers?" scoffed Dandy. "Sure! They charge you $5 for
just answering the phone when you call them up. And $10 to drive over
to your place. And $25 to walk up the front walk."

"Dandy, dear," I pleaded, "with my sprained wrist? I wouldn't be the slightest use to you. You and Hortense and I couldn't even carry the empty drawers down, let alone the..."

Old Dandy has just one way of concluding arguments.

"Be here at 1:30!" he barked, and slammed his telephone receiver down with a clatter.

Despite my sprained wrist, which I had done up in an elastic bandage, I drove across the 20 minutes to Dandy's, arriving at 1:30 as stipulated.

Hortense let me in, screwing in her hearing aid.

"He's upstairs," she said. "He wants us up there with him when they arrive."

"When who arrive?" I inquired, hanging up my overcoat.

"The fellows that demonstrate the vacuum cleaners," said Hortense.

"Are you getting a vacuum cleaner?" I exclaimed enthusiastically.

Hortense gave me a withering smile.

"From him?" she asked.

Old Dandy believes in old-fashioned brooms and dusters.

I climbed the stairs and found Dandy standing in the hall beside the ancient roll-top desk. He was in his shirt sleeves.

"We'll all three," he announced, "be up here when they ring. I want you, Greg, to go down and let them in."

"Who are they?" I queried.

"Vacuum-cleaner salesmen," said Dandy, "trying to sell me a vacuum cleaner. I telephoned two of them to get here at exactly 2 o'clock."

"Why two?" I asked.

"It'll take two of them to wrestle this desk down those stairs," said Dandy, impatiently. "Now, listen..."

"You mean you telephoned two COMPETING vacuum-cleaner people...?" I hazarded.

"Certainly," said Dandy. "Wait till you see how it works. Now, remember..."

There was a ring on the doorbell.

"Psst!" hissed Dandy. "Go down and let him in. And let him see that bandage on your wrist."

"Dandy, I don't like..." I hesitated.

"Hortense," he commanded, "come back around here. And as he comes up the stairs, you and me will be heaving and pushing at the back end."

Hortense unstuffed her hearing aid and put on a very muscular expression.

I opened the door.

"Mr. Daniels?" said a nice-looking young man who had a vacuum cleaner in his hand.

"No," I said. "Mr. Daniels is engaged at the moment. Won't you come in?"

The young fellow came in.

"Hey? Who's that?" called Dandy from the top of the stairs.

He included a few heaves and heavy grunts in the inquiry.

"It's a young man," I called back, "about a vacuum cleaner."

"Tell him to wait," called Dandy, in a faint voice, "till we get this desk downstairs."

There was another ring at the door. I opened. It was a taller and wider young man, with a large carton obviously containing a vacuum cleaner and parts.

"Mr. Daniels?" he asked.

"No, come in," I said. "Mr. Daniels is engaged at the moment."

He stepped inside the vestibule.

On seeing the other young man, he recoiled.

"Hello, there, Harris," he said.

"Hi, Henderson," said the first young man, taking off his overcoat.

From the top of the stairs came the muffled voice of Dandy.

"Who's that?" he cried.

"A young man," I replied, "to see you."

"What about?" groaned Dandy, obviously in the very agony of lifting some heavy object.

"Vacuum cleaner," called Mr. Henderson, taking off HIS coat.

"Tell them," puffed Dandy, "we'll be down in a few minutes. But you come up here and help poor old Hortense and me lift this desk."

I started up the stairs.

"Desk, did he say?" asked young Mr. Harris solicitously.

"Look, we'll lend a hand," said Mr. Henderson, taking off his suit coat as well.

We marched upstairs. There in the dim hall were Dandy and Hortense, their hair tumbled, their faces flushed with exertion, heaving at the back end of the roll-top desk.

"Now, now, sir!" protested young Mr. Harris on perceiving Dandy.

"Don't YOU try to lift anything, with that wrist," said Mr. Henderson to me.

It was quite a job. With Dandy issuing directions and orders, and

Hortense and me skirmishing around with suggestions and observations, the two young men hoisted and heaved and lowered away, and got the desk, inch by inch, down the narrow stairway without a single scratch or bump on the wallpaper.

And when it was safely ensconced in its new location in the far corner of Dandy's living room, we all sat down, Hortense brewed up a pot of tea for all hands, and then we had a splendid demonstration and sales talk from the two young gentlemen representing rival manufacturers of vacuum cleaners.

At the conclusion of which, old Dandy thanked them both, and helped them on with their coats.

"I'll let you know," he said, gratefully fingering the business cards they provided for him, "when I make up my mind. Don't call me, I'll call you."

"Dandy," I declared, when I had let the two young men out, "you're going to come to a bad end."

"All ends," reflected old Dandy, as he helped me on with MY coat, "are bad."

Dogs

Across the street from our place a dog, a spayed female Boxer, is a member of a doctor's family. She lacks that split-faced exuberance that is characteristic of Boxers, probably because of her enforced spinsterhood. Not six times in two years have we ever heard her bark, and then only on special occasions, such as when a party of young people comes gaily chattering out the doctor's door. And then the Boxer joins the fun by uttering a couple of modest barks, merely to belong, as it were.

Her life has been happy and quiet and without care. She sits in the sun on the stone porch. The postman, the doctor's callers, even such shabby strangers as the men who stuff handbills in the letter slot, come up on the porch and the Boxer merely glances at them, with most unBoxerlike indifference. She never strays up or down the street. As she has seen it, her duty has been to make an occasional round of her own premises, accompany members of the family in and out the front door, see them off with a wistful following gaze, and welcome them home by rising from the door sill and engaging in a silent but most energetic shimmy dance. Then she follows them indoors to hear the news. A perfect lady, just a little blasé.

Five weeks ago, a baby arrived at the doctor's house. One of the daughters, for whom the top floor of the house was converted into an apartment, had her first child. In due course, a baby carriage appears on the stone porch each morning as soon as the sun is high. Tucked in all the pretty robes, the new baby has joined our community. And the Boxer, to its indescribable joy, has suddenly discovered what life is all about. What up until now has been a formless and meaningless void has exploded like a skyrocket into a blaze of glory and significance. For this, she has been sitting and lying around the front door, all these months, years.

The dog is reversed, converted, turned inside out. The door mat, which up until now she had conceived to be merely a convenience for her comfort, she realizes has been a sentry's station all the time, a rampart, a bastion on which a fearless guard must take post. The minute that baby carriage is wheeled out the door, the Boxer, transfigured in bearing, chest out, head up, wide mouth arrogantly spread, struts and stares at the surroundings. Every passer-by is scrutinized intently. Sometimes it is necessary to step off the porch to have a look down the side entrance and glance around the other side of the house. But that takes only an instant; and by the time the mistress has tucked the baby in and put the brake on the carriage, the Boxer is back on the porch ready to take over. When the door closes, and she is left alone, an indescribable look of pride descends upon her. For four or five minutes, she just stands, savoring the splendor of it, ears pricked, watching every movement in the street, every car, every pedestrian. Then, warily, she reclines on the door mat, her forelegs and paws extended in front of the baby carriage.

And no one, friend or stranger, can come up the walk or mount the steps without the Boxer rising sharp and shrewd, a Boxer indeed, and uttering an instant challenge, a brief, commanding bark. Even members of the family are suspect. They have to stand and give the countersign, the password. When the baby wakes and cries, the Boxer leaps up and paces anxiously back and forth on the porch. And if no one comes, she goes and scratches on the door.

Spinster, indeed? She is an Amazon, all of a sudden. Maybe more. In her simple, ancient mind she imagines she is a mother.

After watching the Boxer for a few days, I was out in a secluded bit of forest a few miles north of the city on the weekend ramble to greet the first snow. Right in the thick of the bush, I came upon a most curious thing—a solitary lilac bush, a good big one, surrounded by a ring of iris, the leaves protruding stoutly from the wintry ground. It was a patch such as you might find in a city garden. But by no stretch of the imagination could you suppose that once upon a time a house had stood here in the midst of the woods. The land is rough and rocky. What a curious place for a lilac bush, and a wide circle of iris.

At the farmhouse beyond the end of the woodlot, I inquired about the lilac bush.

"Oh, that's been there for years," said the woman. "It's a dog's grave. A hound's. A lawyer used to hunt all through here, years ago. His favorite hound died, so he brought it there and buried it, and put those things on the grave."

"Who was the lawyer?" I asked.

"I only remember he was a lawyer," she said.

I wonder if anything blooms in season on the lawyer's grave, and if anyone remembers it.

The buds are strong on the lilac bush, the iris leaves are sturdy. There will be a bright glow in that clearing each spring.

Some people think a lot of dogs.

The Boxer across the road helps to fathom it.

The Blue Box

N OT NOSY, exactly, but observant, would best describe a newspaperman. Observant, out of the corner of his eye.

For example, my wife told me to pick her up three pair of her
favorite nylons while I was downtown.

When I worked my way through the crowded department store—it
was Friday—to the hosiery section, I was miffed to discover there was
some kind of a sale on, and the ladies (and a few gents), were packed
three and four deep the full length of the counter.

If I were not a newspaperman, I would have said the hell with it, and
come back next day. But a newspaperman is bound by the ethics of his
profession to participate in all the griefs as well as all the joys of the
public he serves. Besides, when my wife wants three pair of nylons, she
wants three pair of nylons.

It was interesting to get into the jam. It was amusing to watch the
ladies, young, middle-aged and old, jockeying for position. It took me
eight minutes to get from the rear of the crowd, at its thinnest point, into
the second row from the counter. It took me 10 minutes to manoeuvre
from the second row into the line along the counter. This was done only,
of course, by taking the firmest stand, and not allowing either muscular
young women to butt me aside, or pitiable old ladies, muttering and
moaning, to chivvy me out of my rightful position. One of the only
occasions on which elderly ladies try to pretend they are old is in a
bargain crush.

I had just reached the counter, and was standing firm, waiting to catch
one of the salesgirls' eye, when, over my shoulder came a clear, fluty
feminine voice above the low hubbub of the crowd:

"Oh, pardon me, miss! But did I leave a small blue box here on the
counter?"

I turned. The lady was not in the row next back of me. She was right at
the back. On the outside of the throng. She was a well-dressed, self-

possessed lady of about 40, with an easy commanding air about her.

"A small blue box...?" she trilled musically.

The salesgirl, who was just about to wait on me next, looked over our heads to the lady.

"A blue box? I'll inquire, ma'am."

The sale was held up while the girl went and questioned her fellow clerks. A manager came around the end of the counter and joined the colloquy. They came along and spoke over our heads.

"We haven't seen any blue box, ma'am," said the clerk. "Did you leave it here, you think?"

"I can't be sure," said the lady. "It was a tiny blue box, about this... Pardon me!"

Politely, with an inclination of the head, she eased herself past the two people back of me and squashed in beside me.

"I'm dreadfully sorry to hold things up like this," she smiled graciously around at us all. "But it was a valuable little parcel. Blue, you know. You're sure you didn't notice it?"

"Quite sure, ma'am. But if you'll just go up to the lost-and-found office, and leave a description..."

"Yes. I shall do that. But now that I'm here, I wonder would you just let me have four pair of these nylons on sale, size 9½; a fairly dark shade..."

I turned around and looked one after the other at the faces near me. None of them appeared to mind.

But when she got her nylons, and assured the salesgirl and all of us that she would go straightaway to the lost-and-found office and report her loss of the blue box, I decided, as a newspaperman, not a nosy one, you understand, but an observant one, to let my wife's nylons go, and follow the gracious lady.

She did not go to the lost-and-found.

She wandered around the store, looking at a great variety of things— lamp shades, some pillow slips, glass tumblers, cotton dress goods, striped, and a rack of housecoats. She was not in a hurry.

Neither was I.

While looking at the housecoats, she spotted, with the lithe look of a lioness spotting a gazelle moving on the veldt, a crowd of women swarming about a counter half way across the ladies' lingerie department. Without an instant's hesitation, she dropped the housecoat she was handling, and headed for the melee, I in hot pursuit.

153

I stood a little back. It was a lingerie sale. From the outskirts of the crowd, the lady stood on tiptoe, peering, straining, to see and appraise the nature of the goods on sale.

Apparently she was interested. She began to close in, at the thinnest point in the crowd. I closed in too.

"Pardon me!" she called out, clear and fluty, as a salesgirl hove within hail. "Pardon me, but did I leave a small blue box here on the counter a few moments ago?"

There was the same momentary pause of attention around her. Ladies are always interested in the loss of a blue box. Especially a small blue box. It suggests something valuable—jewelry, earrings, perfume, maybe.

"A small blue box," warbled the lady, holding her hand up high to show the size of the box above the heads of the ladies in front of her.

She started to edge in past them.

"Pardon me, lady," I sang out, "but I think you left that small blue box down at the hosiery counter, on the main floor, didn't you?"

The lady recoiled. She stared at me with intense distaste.

"I beg your pardon!" she said haughtily.

But I had unnerved her. She abandoned her attack. She strode away from the sale, and I followed her far enough to see she wasn't going to the lost-and-found.

But you see the sort of service we newspapermen render you innocent public?

Always watch out for lofty ladies looking for small blue boxes. They'll chivvy you out of your turn every time.

The Model

W HEN A GIRL passes 18 and gets to be 20 or 20½—I am
referring to her dress size, not her age—finding a pretty dress
becomes a fairly grim job. All the beautiful fabrics and textiles
are routed by the manufacturers into clothes for the 12s, 14s and 16s.
What's left over goes into the clothes you see on the racks where the
forlorn matrons grope.

It is many a year since my wife finally surrendered from 18 and moved
to size 20. And then, in due time, she moved inexorably into that size
invented by the clothing trade for the peace of mind of the 22s. It is
called 20½.

Whenever we are downtown together, we make a casual round of the
dress departments of the big stores and often will try a short whirl in
some of the specialty shops that feature raiment for the well-built. You
never can tell when miracles will happen. Maybe sometime some dress
manufacturer might go nuts and put an attractive fabric in a 20½.

The fashion salon in the big department store is at the far end of the
dress department. It is a semi-circular foyer, artistically done up in long
gilt drapes, mushroom broadloom from wall to wall, tall mirrors, several
little gilt chairs and gilt settees for the customers to sit on while being
attended. Off this foyer, the try-on cubicles are curtained.

I selected one of the little gilt chairs, took off my hat and rested my
hands on the crook of my stick. My wife was taken in tow by one of the
ladies of the fashion salon, a 20½ herself, as a matter of fact, but
fortunately free to dress in smart mercantile black.

The two of them picked half a dozen frocks off the salon's exclusive
hangers and vanished into a cubicle.

Across from me, on a gilt settee, sat a pleasant-looking middle-aged
lady. She gave me a shy smile, and dropped her eyes. I wondered who
she was waiting for. There appeared to be no other customers in the
cubicles.

After a few minutes, my wife came out, arrayed in one of the selected dresses. If it had had a little more color and zip to it, it would have been a beauty. Indeed, it was a beauty anyway, despite its sombre colors.

"Take it!" I cried enthusiastically. "It's smart. It really is smart. If it had a little color, a little zip, now..."

But my wife turned it down, and in a few minutes came out of the cubicle in her own clothes, and wearing that expression familiar to the faces of the 20½.

We had lunch. We visited one other department store and three small specialty dress shops without finding a thing. Not anything.

"I'll go back," said my wife, "and take one more look at that one you liked."

So back we went to the gilded fashion salon and my wife found the same saleslady. And as I took my seat in the same little gilt chair, removing my hat, I noted with surprise that the same pleasant middle-aged lady I had seen before lunch was still sitting on the gilt settee across the foyer.

We smiled.

"Are you an employee here?" I inquired, always interested in employees and curious activities, such as sitting dressed like a customer on a gilt settee all day.

"Mercy, no," replied the lady. "I am just trying to select a dress."

"Well," I exclaimed, "is there nobody waiting on you?"

I was half prepared to jump up and demand some attention for this pleasant-looking lady.

"No, no," she explained. "I am letting the other customers model for me. Don't you see? Professional models are of no earthly use to people of my age, of course. So when I want a new dress, I just come down here and sit for an hour or two."

"Good grief!" I protested.

"Oh, I've had lunch since I saw you," she hastened happily. "But I just sit and watch other customers, especially people my age and size. They try the dresses on, and come out here to look in the long mirrors, or to show the dresses to their friends..."

"And husbands," I agreed. "I think you've got a wonderful idea."

"It works beautifully," admitted the lady. "Your wife is just my size."

At this moment, my wife, wearing a new dress I hadn't seen before, came disconsolately out of the cubicle and stood gazing doubtfully at me.

"Where's the one you tried on before lunch?" I complained.

"Sold!" said my wife, hollowly. "It's been sold."

"Yes, I bought it," said the pleasant lady on the gold settee.

"You?" I cried.

"Your wife is the best model I've had for years," assured the lady. "Exactly my style. I happened to see you in the elevator a few moments ago, and I figured you were heading back here. So I came too, in the hope that your wife might model a few more dresses."

"Well!" said my wife, glancing down at the one she had on.

"If you're not taking that one," said the pleasant lady, "I'd be most interested..."

"I'm taking it!" my wife informed her firmly.

Which she did.

But it's just another 20½.

The Rug

W E WERE sitting in the McEwens' living room last Sunday afternoon, as usual, when Mae McEwen suddenly leaped to her feet, staring out the window, and cried:

"The rug! The rug!"

Her husband bounded upright, glanced out the window and immediately galloped across the room toward the staircase.

"Where is it?" he hissed.

"Top shelf," cried his wife. "Linen closet!"

Bill McEwen vanished up the stairs at top speed.

My wife and I stood up to look out the window, too. A middle-aged gentleman was assisting a middle-aged lady out of a handsome black motor car out in front.

"It's the Bilburys," explained Mae. "You've met them."

"So what?" I demanded.

Mr. Bilbury closed the car door and took Mrs. Bilbury's arm to escort her up the slightly icy walk.

"Mae!" Bill called urgently from upstairs. "It isn't on the top shelf. Quick! Where is it?"

"Look under the towels," cried Mae.

"What the Sam Hill?" I inquired.

"The Bilburys," explained Mae, "brought us a rug from Mexico a year ago. The darndest looking..."

The bell rang.

"I'll wait a minute," said Mae, calmly, listening to the sounds of Bill's feet hastily scampering up above. "He's found it. Sit down. Relax. Look casual..."

My wife and I sat down, and Mae went and opened the door.

"Why, hell-O!" she cried.

So we had to turn off the radio, the Carnegie Hall symphony, to which we had been listening, while the Bilburys took off their coats and

158

disposed themselves comfortably.

Bill, who had come very quietly down the back stairs, appeared heartily from the kitchen.

"Hell-O!" he greeted. "I was just putting the kettle on."

"You were listening to the symphony?" said Mrs. Bilbury. "I do hope we aren't disturbing you."

"Not at ALL!"

But they were, of course. We come over every Sunday to the McEwens, who have the best radio, and have tea and symphony; and then, about 6, the McEwens come over to our place, where we have the best TV; and at the end of the evening, we have Spanish-onion sandwiches and stuff.

"NOT at all!" we all lied, politely.

So we sat there, while the Bilburys outlined the trip to Florida they are taking next week. They're very comfortably off. Nice people for the McEwens to know. Nice big car to stand out in front of anybody's home on a Sunday afternoon.

Well, in due course, the Bilburys got up to leave, and Mrs. Bilbury had to just run upstairs for a minute. So the girls went with her, and we could hear them exclaiming over the rug, which Bill had so hastily spread in the bedroom.

"It does suit the room," I heard Mrs. Bilbury's voice, made for gracious living, billowing along the hall and down the stairs.

So after the Bilburys had left, we all went up to see the rug before Bill folded it and put it back in the linen closet.

I wouldn't want it, either. It is Mexican. And the Mexicans can figure out the most fantastic clashes of mauve and henna.

"Well," I said, "we'll run on ahead. You folks follow whenever you're ready."

"We'll be right behind you," said Mae.

My wife and I hastily threw our coats on and went out to our car.

"I hope not," breathed my wife, as we got in.

"Eh?"

"I hope they aren't right behind us," she repeated. "Make it snappy."

Now, I don't like driving fast on these nasty, icy, rutty streets. And Bill McEwen is a much faster driver than I am. But, you see, we had to get home in plenty of time to get out the picture and hang it in place of the other one in the living room.

The McEwens' nephew is an art student. And two Christmases ago, they presented us with one of the young fellow's masterpieces. It is a landscape. It is about a barn, and a snake fence, and a pasture field. It is awful.

We keep it, glass side to the wall, in the clothes closet downstairs. And whenever the McEwens are coming, we take down the very pretty print of a Belgian canal which hangs over our mantelpiece, and which goes so nicely with our living room, and hang the McEwen opus there.

"Make it snappy," urged my wife.

We made it, all right. It was pretty skiddy and bouncy. But we made it, and we hustled into the house.

I made for the cupboard and got the masterpiece out, while my wife took down the Belgian canal. Like trained personnel in a straight-line production industry, we passed, I to the mantel, she to the clothes closet.

Up went the picture.

Closed went the clothes-closet door.

Click-swish went our front door, and in walked Mae and Bill.

"We just got in the door." I cried.

We all took off our coats together.

"Well," said Mae, going over and standing before the mantel to view with pride her nephew's chef d'oeuvre.

"A picture," said Bill, "MAKES a room, don't you think?"

"You're dead right," I agreed, going over and switching on the TV.

───────────◆───────────

The Roughneck

BILL HAWES, my schoolboy chum and comrade of World War I—that's the one back there near the Boer War—has made a great deal of money in his lifetime, despite the fact that he is one of the softest-spoken, least aggressive of men. When I was a sergeant, he was a private. When I was a lieutenant, he was a sergeant; I a major, he a lieutenant. The difference was that I had a loud voice and a domineering manner. I guess you don't have to have a loud voice and a domineering manner to make money.

I saw Bill coming toward me in the noon-hour crowd. He was walking a little dejected, and his eyes were on the pavement.

"Bill!" I said.

"Oh, hello," said he, pausing to shake.

"You look," I informed him, "as if you had lost your pet pocketknife."

"Well," heaved Bill, "I am in a bit of a snit. I'm sorry if it shows..."

Then he drew me over against the trust company building to get out of the foot traffic.

"Look!" he said, brightening. "You're the very man!"

"Well, now," I said, flattered, because I am not in the habit of having wealthy people tell me that.

"You've always had a loud, assertive manner," said Bill. "It gets you places. You make yourself heard."

"Yeah, but..." I reminded him.

"Tell me this," demanded Bill intently. "Who gets the better of you? Think now! Where does your loudness fail you? Honest. There must be some times you don't get by with a blustery approach."

"Well," I reflected, "in church. I don't cut much ice in church. Funerals. I'm not much good at funerals. Subdued, you know!"

I thought of all the situations in which it is impossible to be myself.

"In hospitals," I remembered. "Calling on people in hospitals. You

161

have to pipe down. I'm not much of a success as a hospital visitor. I don't subdue very well..."

"You've got it!" cried Bill Hawes, much more excited than you usually see him. "Look here. I am just in the throes of working out a merger of three small companies."

Bill is a director of about 20 companies.

"But the president of one of the three," went on Bill, "is a loud, aggressive, bullying type of man. He is holding everything up. We have had five meetings. And he dominates every one of them. Noisy, domineering. He shouts. We can't get anywhere with him. My dear old boy, you've solved the whole thing!"

"How?" I asked modestly.

"I'll let you know," he cried.

Just after supper two nights later, Bill Hawes telephoned me.

"Have you ever been a shareholder?" he asked. "A director?"

"Not so far," I confessed.

"Well, you're going to be one tonight," said he. "Just for tonight. Can you come to my place at eight?"

I arrived at Bill's beautiful big home at five to eight and a maid answered the door.

"Would you come in quietly, sir?" she whispered. "Mrs. Hawes has been taken ill with an attack of her tic dollyroo..."

We tiptoed in through the spacious hall, and she led me to the library. Bill was in there with four other men, all conversing, in low tones.

"This is Mr. Clark, one of my personal advisers," said Bill.

In the next 10 or 15 minutes, seven other men arrived, led in all very hushed by the maid. One of them was a thickset, bald-headed man with keen, darting eyes...

"Gentlemen," said Bill. "I'm extremely sorry. When I suggested we meet here tonight, I had no idea Mrs. Hawes was going to have one of her attacks. It didn't come on until after supper, so I had no opportunity to cancel the arrangement..."

There were murmurs and clucks of sympathy from all.

"I think," said Bill, "we can conduct our business without disturbing her..."

I was right. The bald-headed guy with the Airedale eyes was Mr. Roughneck. He cleared his throat. Before the group had got themselves suitably seated in a circle around Bill's big library, he had got very red in the face. He spoke in a hoarse whisper, and even that caused the others to glance at him and make little signals to pipe down. They all produced briefcases and took out sheaves of papers. In low tones, they picked up the business in hand where it had been left off at the adjourned meetings.

Mr. Hoarse sat forward on the edge of his chair and tried to employ his chin, his eyes and his whole face in lieu of his voice. He used his arms in violent punching gestures, to lend strength to his muted voice. But he was weaponless. Without his voice, he was hamstrung. The others, speaking quietly, seemed to have far greater force in what they had to say. The meeting progressed. Mr. Sergeant-Major sat back in his chair, baffled. Bill would turn to me from time to time and ask me if I understood the situation so far.

"Clearly," I said, with dignity.

The meeting lasted an hour and three-quarters. It was all entirely over my head. All I had to do was sit back and look shrewd and nod wisely from time to time at the tycoons.

Before it was over, I felt sorry for the poor old roughrider. Many a time, I had felt the way he was feeling. By the time the maid brought in refreshments, he was breathing deeply and I thought he might have apoplexy. The merger was signed. His hand trembled with the pen.

Quietly, they all left, shaking hands warmly. I lingered.

"O.K.!" yelled Bill up the stairs.

Down the stairs bounded Mrs. Hawes.

"Did it work?" she cried.

"I'm going to give Greg a hundred shares in the new company," proclaimed Bill, giving me a hug.

But I haven't got them yet. You don't get rich giving things away.

The Elusive Blue

THE gravel road we were on was mucky, slippery and full of puddles. The man driving the car was the most pig-headed of my friends. When another car came in view behind us, my friend put on a little more speed.

"Easy," I said.

"Who wants to get splashed?" snorted my friend, putting on still more speed, so that we bounced and sloshed on the narrow road. I watched the ditches. They were full of sleet and mud.

The car behind drew slowly nearer. It had the look of a country car, accustomed to such roads as this. We were city slickers.

"Let him pass," I suggested.

Instead, we accelerated. But in a couple of hundred yards, the car behind drew close enough to sound its horn commandingly. We had to bow to superior driving. My friend slackened speed and drew cautiously over to the right. In a shower of mud, the conqueror slashed past.

"Yah!" said my friend.

One half mile ahead, the right shoulder of the road had collapsed. The incessant early winter rains had washed out, without warning, a hole three feet deep and running half-way across the road. The car that had passed us saw it too late. It went into the washout, broke its steering gear and bounced crazily out into the fields, rolling over. I sat with the two badly-injured farm boys in the rain while my friend drove, shaken and thanking God out of the corner of his mouth, for help.

Such instances of narrow squeaks due to sheer chance are commonplace in all our lives. The extent to which accident and chance enter into all human endeavor is not honestly admitted by us. We like to think we figure everything out, unaided. But a list of even the greatest discoveries in science and industry that are due not to luck but to mistakes and blunders would be a really comical reflection on human nature. The most ridiculous one I know was confessed to me by a chemical engineer.

Artists are more afraid of blue than of any other color they employ in their paintings. The manufacturers of artists' colors take the greatest pains to insure fidelity in their various shades and degrees of blue. Expert chemists have a hand in their preparation.

At one well-known factory, a batch of ultramarine blue came out a surprise. It was not ultramarine, however. It was a curiously beautiful and rich variation of ultramarine. Too beautiful, in fact, to be dumped down the drain; so the makers gave it a new name, and put it up in tubes and sent it on to the market.

It was an instantaneous success. Repeat orders began to pour in.

But there wasn't any more.

When the orders mounted up to really important proportions, the management realized they had hold of a good thing. They called in the chemists and had them analyze a few tubes of the accident that they were able to rescue from the jobbers and wholesalers.

Despite every try on the part of the chemists and the technical staff, they could not recapture the curious and exciting shade of blue that had mysteriously come from that one particular vat.

Still the orders poured in. A full-dress investigation was staged. Everybody in the business who was associated with the production of the freak mixture was assembled. The seriousness of the situation was explained. Everybody was urged to try to remember what had happened that particular day on which the vat was produced.

"By golly," broke in the workman who had been attending the mixing on that occasion. "I wonder if that was the day I dropped my lunch into the vat?"

The chemists leaped.

The lunch had consisted of a cheese sandwich, a sliced onion sandwich, a cold sausage and a piece of fruit cake. The bread was brown. The lunch was wrapped in newspaper.

Now, you may suppose that workman, with the rank of at least vice-president, now had to bring his lunch every day and drop it into the vat.

That is the way I would do; and probably you, too. But science is wonderful. The chemists analyzed the lunch, added the necessary chemical ingredients; and lo, the mysterious blue!

How much of the tragedy, the fun and the profit of life is sheer mischance?

Ploomoot

I F YOU are a ship's steward, a cabin steward, it must be quite a gamble, each trip, on the sort of passengers you draw.

My steward was deeply unimpressed by me when I turned up in one of the fancy first-class cabins of which he was the custodian.

The ship was the Ile de France and the steward's name was Jean. He was a tall, lean, aristocratic Gaul who had the faintly distant airs of the conductor of a symphony orchestra. His cabins were all of the choice first class, and he had the right to expect fairly important, not to say affluent, passengers. Normally, I do not travel in such style; but I was on a hurry-up trip to Rome. I had to take last-minute accommodation; and all that was available was the best. Besides, I had to do some writing while on board.

Jean came in and looked me and my baggage over with ill-concealed disdain.

"Your trunk, monsieur?"

"I have no trunk," I confessed. "Just this suitcase, the haversack, and my typewriter here..."

Jean muttered to himself, breathed deeply, and went sadly out the door, shutting it after him as though to prevent neighboring passengers catching a glimpse of his ill fortune.

When I went out to look over my fellow-passengers and share in the excitement of departure, with New York's skyline to bid adieu, Jean was just ushering a party of one middle-aged gentleman and two middle-aged ladies breathlessly into one of the adjoining cabins in my corridor. They were obviously tycoons and tycoonesses, and Jean was ceremonious. He gave me a slanting glance, to suggest that THIS was the sort of thing he was accustomed to.

Our relations did not improve during the first couple of days at sea. He brought me tea, at my request, first thing in the morning; but any attempt at generalities on my part was swiftly cut short.

"Pardon me, monsieur, but I have many things to attend."

He tidied up my cabin each morning, but always while I was out. Whenever I passed him standing with other stewards in the main corridor, Jean would give me a thin, bare smile; and one morning I overheard him remark apologetically to his fellows stewards as I passed:

"Journaliste."

About the fourth day out, finished with my writing, I rang for Jean.

He opened the door and stood without, enquiringly inclined.

"What day do we get to Le Havre?" I asked.

I pronounced it in the fashion we had pronounced it millions of us, in the old First War. I called it Le Harve, as in Harvey.

Jean recoiled. He placed his hand on his brow.

"No, no, no, monsieur," he groaned. "NOT Le Harve. It is Le Havre!"

He projected his head inside the cabin so that I could observe the motions of his lips as he pronounced it for me.

"Loo-ahvrrr!" he said. "Loo-ahvrrr!"

The rrr was a brief, impossible trill of sound, a mere trip, a flip of an R.

"Loo-ahvrrr!" he repeated. "Say it!"

"Luh-haver," I said.

Jean entered my cabin, shut the door.

"No, no, NO! Monsieur, look: Loo-ahvrr. It is very simple. Do not say luh. Say loo. Loo-ahvre, all one sound, all one word, very sweet, very smooth, like this: Looahvre!"

"Loo-havruh."

"No! Leave out the ash."

"The ash?"

"Huh," said Jean, brushing back his hair out of his eyes, and glancing about my cabin. He straightened my shaving things on the tray above the basin, and rehung my haversack more symmetrically on its hook.

"The ash," he said. "The huh. Do not sound the huh. I do not know the English word for ash."

"Ah!" I cried. "The aitch!"

"What a horrible sound," said Jean. "Very good. Do not sound that thing. Listen most carefully. It is one sound, all run together, smooth and beautiful. See: Looahvrrr."

"Loo-ahvrrr."

"Good! But do not pause after the loo."

"Looahvrrr," I said.

Jean stood back and regarded me with a personal and kindly expression, the first time, as it were, he had seen me.

"Now, monsieur," he said, with a dramatic gesture of invitation, "ask the question."

"What day," I enunciated carefully, "do we arrive at Looahvrrr?"

"On Thursday, monsieur."

"At what time on Thursday do we arrive at Loo-ahvrrr?"

"At about four o'clock, apres-midi."

"Do we go directly," I pursued, "to Looahvrrr, or do we call at some other port before arrival there?"

"Ah, yes, monsieur," said Jean, "first we call at Ploomoot."

"Ploomoot?" said I.

Jean fell back against the cabin door in chagrin, his arms spread out behind him.

"Ploo," he said huskily, "moot!"

"Plymouth?" I remarked softly.

Jean closed his eyes.

When he opened them, we started to laugh. And we laughed all the two days to Plymouth and all the way on to Le Havre. I gave him a one-pound tip, just as good as the tycoons and tycoonesses next door; and he stole my briar pipe, carved like a walnut, when he was packing my gear.

But that's all right. He wanted a souvenir to remember me, and I had Ploomoot to remember him.

The Tough Men

WHEN a baby was born in my family, or even among my next of kin, I always managed to be far away.

Of course, when it was all over, I rushed back. And nobody could have been more enthusiastic. But now that I am old, I can tell the truth.

It all began when I heard the irate voice of Capt. Curley Davis, the battalion medical officer, a doctor, outside the door of our hut.

"Can anybody tell me," Curley was protesting, "what the devil these people are doing up here? They should be 20 miles back!"

(I speak, of course, of that old first war.)

He pushed open the hut door. Of the five lieutenants getting into our bedrolls, I was the only one with my boots still on.

"Clarkie," said Curley, "get your trench coat on and come out here."

We had just come "down the line," as we said, after 18 days in the trenches, for a six-day rest amid the ruins of the village of Acq, behind Mont St. Eloi. Rest! And tomorrow we would have a bath. We stank.

Outside I found Curley Davis, two soldiers, and a ragged-looking civilian, a Frenchman.

"As far as we can make out," said Curley, who was still carrying his big haversack with the leather bottom, "this Frenchman's daughter is having a baby."

A baby! What a ridiculous suggestion in this place of desolation, with the winter sky flickering as with summer sheet lightning from the guns a little to the east.

What's that word the old boy keeps repeating," Curley asked the two soldiers.

"Retourné," said one.

"Par les pieds," said the other.

The old Frenchman repeated the words hoarsely excitedly. I could see

now he was shaking, more than from the cold.

"That means," I said, "turned over. And by the feet."

"Oh, Lord!" cried Curley, backing up. "A breech birth!"

"Breech?"

"Wrong end first," said Curley.

"Can we go now, sir?" asked the soldiers, loaded with all their equipment.

When they had slogged off, Curley had me recheck by questioning the old man in my army French.

How far? Half a kilometre down the Aubigny road, here. How long had she been in labor? Since early morning. (Curley and I checked our luminous wrist watches. It was past midnight. Sixteen, 16 hours?) How old is she? Eighteen. Who is with her. Her mother. Where's her husband? With the French army, artillery, down by Verdun. Have they a stove? No. Fire? Yes, a fireplace. Water? Yes, a *puits,* a well with a pump. Are there no French people around, anybody to help, any midwife? *Sage-femme?* The mother is a *sage-femme!* There is nobody they can find.

"Now, look!" said Curley. "I have never handled a confinement in my life! I sent my medical sergeant out of the line at noon ahead of us to drive the medical cart back to Corps to be refitted."

The medical cart was the horse-drawn vehicle that carried all the medical, surgical and first-aid equipment for 1,000 men.

"All I've got," said Curley, slapping his big haversack, "is this. No anesthetic, no instruments."

It would have the black japanned tin box with the medical officer's collection of pills; a few essential surgical instruments; some bandages, lint.

"Curley," I said, with the calmness of the infantry lieutenant, "hand it over to the brigade Field Ambulance. They've got a bunch of doctors..."

They also had motor ambulances. We were, of course, horse-drawn.

"Don't be crazy," said Curley. "Nobody knows where they are. They are on the move, the way we are."

"Now, look, Curley; we can go up to the main road and flag down a lorry. They could take her back to Bruay, or some place, where there would be a convent or something..."

Curley went out and stood in the road. The old Frenchman leaned against the hut wall, muttering and moaning. He thought he was losing.

It was a long time after, when I was older and wiser, that I knew what Capt. Curley Davis was doing there standing in the dark, stiff and straight. He was remembering an ancient Greek (about 400 years before Christ, by the name of Hippocrates).

"Where's your platoon?" he asked, coming back.

"Aw, Curley," I said, "down the road here a little way. But I only put them to bed half an hour..."

Curley led off, signalling the old Frenchman to follow.

"I want two good men," said Curley. "Two TOUGH men."

I had 'em. Old Sixteen Platoon. The Steel Trap Gang we called ourselves, to the amusement of the rest of the battalion. But I don't know!

We came to the sour hut where my platoon was billeted. I had already picked my two tough men. Pte. Post, first. He was tough; he was young; he was part Negro; he was arrogant, irrepressible. Nobody had ever seen him flinch.

And then my Lewis gunner, Pte. Hayden. Fairly tall, lean, with small, hard gray eyes. He had no passion for King and Country. He had passion only for the black tube of his Lewis gun, that bassoon of death. I was a little afraid of Pte. Hayden.

When I pushed open the hut door, there were still a couple of candles burning. I think they knew who I was looking for, though many of them were already asleep. They had their puttees and boots off but, fully clothed, were under their blankets, with their muddy greatcoats spread above, in the chicken-wire bunks.

"Post?" I said, quietly.

Pte. Post sat up.

"Hayden?" I asked.

Post got up, in his socks, and poked Pte. Hayden. Hayden sat up and bumped his head on the chicken wire above. Pte. Bowers, with the broad cheekbones and the inextinguishable grin, stuck his head over the bunk.

"They'll be here in a minute," I said to Curley, when I went out.

The three of them came. Pte. Bowers had to be in on all activities concerned with Post and Hayden.

We turned and went back toward the road to Aubigny.

After a few paces came the dry voice of Pte. Hayden.

"What time is it? Is this a working party? Sir?"

He always put the Sir in, though reluctantly.

"Men," said Curley, "this French civilian's daughter is having a baby."

"Jesus!" said Pte. Post, not profanely, but reverently.

"I'll want you to get a lot of wood," said Curley as we marched over the slimy road. "A lot of water. I've got to boil a lot of water. But I may want you to help hold her."

There was no sound but of our boots on the mud.

Curley glanced over his shoulder.

"You," he said to Pte. Bowers, who was the shortest of the bunch, except myself, "will hold her shoulders. You [that was Hayden] hold one ankle; and you [that was Post] the other."

We trod in silence 50 yards.

"In the delivery rooms," said Curley "—I'm remembering the book—in the delivery rooms they have operating tables and straps and ankle clamps."

We did another 50 yards. How dark it was! How menacing!

"I may as well tell you," said Curley, "that this may be a very difficult job."

For another few hundred yards, no sound but our feet. Then the old Frenchman led us into a short lane at the end of which was a squat broken stone cottage. There was no glass in its windows, of course, only old cloth and paper. As we neared, there came an eerie, wild sound, like a coyote far off on the lone prairie.

"Jesus," said Pte. Post again, still reverently, and placed the heels of his hands against his ears.

"Wait here," said Curley, and the old man opened the door and led him into the dimly lit interior.

In less than a minute he opened the door.

"Two of you get wood," he said.

"I don't care where you get it. Get wood. Anything, I will be responsible. Two of you carry water. The old man is bringing pails."

I detailed Ptes. Hayden and Bowers to get wood. They would know. Fences. Window frames. Doors. I kept Pte. Post to carry water with me. He had a special attitude toward lieutenants. He was humorous. They come, and they go, he used to say.

We carried water.

"Take it in," I said, holding the door open.

"YOU take it in, sir," said Pte. Post, setting down his iron pots.

They brought wood, all broken up ready for the fire.

"Take it in," I said to Ptes. Hayden and Bowers.

They dumped their armfuls in my arms. "YOU take it in, sir."

When I came out, Pte. Post, was squatting alone, his back against the cottage wall, his elbows on his knees, the heels of his hands jamming his ears. There were faint sounds of sobbing; now and again a faint cry.

"Where," I demanded, "are Hayden and Bowers?"

"They buzzed off," said Pte. Post, only using that other word.

"Why, the..." I began; but remembered the proper attitude of an officer to his men.

I joined Post, sitting with my back to the wall, hands clamped on ears.

The first to return was Pte. Bowers. He was carrying something white across his arms.

"The Captain," said Bowers, "was saying there wasn't a sheet, a pillow case, a clean bit of cotton..."

"What have you got there?"

"Sheets, sir," said Pte. Bowers. "Them big howitzer battery officers always got white sheets in their bedrolls. There's a big how battery back the road."

"Good for you!" I cried. "How did you get them?"

"They don't know I got them," explained Pte. Bowers.

"Take them in! Take them in!" I exulted.

"YOU take them in, sir," said Bowers, unloading.

When I came out, Pte. Hayden was coming in the lane with something glowing. It was a brazier, with a bail, or handle. And in his other hand was a sandbag full of coke.

"Grand!" I cried. "Where did you get it?"

"At the guard room," said Pte. Hayden.

"Did they mind?"

"They were asleep," explained Pte. Hayden.

"Take it in, take it in!" I headed for the door.

"YOU take it in, sir."

In the faint light, as I opened the door, and took the bail from Pte. Hayden, I caught his eyes.

From the inner room, the old woman, crippled, ("Sciatica," Curley explained) came with gestures of joy and set one of the larger pots on the brazier, after I filled it with coke. We blew on the holes.

Then I went out and joined my tough men.

The door opened.

"I gave her some morphia," said Curley. "I may need you shortly. Stand by, eh?"

Stand? We sat.

It seemed a long time. Pte. Hayden got up and walked down the lane where he paced back and forward. I went down to see him.

"O.K.?" I asked.

It was good to have met his eyes, even, after all.

"How old are you, Hayden?" I asked conversationally.

"Twenty-six," he said, "sir."

"Married?"

"Yessir!" rather thick.

"Any children?"

"Oh, God, NO!" cried Pte. Hayden, whirling from me. "Thank God, NO!"

I went back and rejoined Ptes. Post and Bowers.

In a few minutes the door opened.

"Well, gentlemen," said Capt. Davis, using the inclusive noun, "it's all over. Everything fine. A little girl!"

Pte. Hayden came running from the lane.

"We don't have to...?" said Pte. Post, striking a military stance.

"No," said Curley.

The old Frenchman came to the door behind Curley and asked me to invite the *soldats* in to see the baby.

We filed in through the battered main room to the side room where, in the candle light, lay the young woman, her eyes drowsy from Curley's pills. The old woman, hobbling, lifted the tiny bundle from the bed, in its torn strips of Pte. Bower's sheets.

In silence, we looked at the small purple face she unveiled to us.

We filed out.

"Well, men," I said, "you can go back to billets. I'll wait for Capt. Davis."

They sloshed out the lane.

In a little while, Curley, haversack and all, came out, and we marched in silence back out the road and up towards Acq.

With the curiosity of the laity in such matters, I said:

"Tell me, how did you... uh... manage?"

"By the book," said Capt. Curley Davis, with all the frankness and ethics of his profession.

When we came abreast of Sixteen Platoon's hut, I plucked Curley's sleeve and halted him. I executed a stiff right turn, stamped my left heel, and saluted into the night.

"Good men, eh?" agreed Curley, giving a little Medical Corps salute.

"I never," I said, as we moved on, "saw three more scared men!"

"Oho," said Capt. Curley Davis. "And who ELSE?"

"O.K.,"I retorted indignantly. "And who ELSE?"

So we shook hands when we came to my hut and Curley went on to his hut, up near battalion H.Q.

Thus, at the age of 24, an officer and a gentleman, I learned something fundamental about tough men.

Under certain circumstances, tough men can be as tough as need be. But under other circumstances, they can fall apart, like little boys. And finally, at certain times, a man may be forgiven if he goes far off, some place, and hides his face in his hands.